Venture Into Darkness

ALICE TISDALE HOBART

Venture

Into

Darkness

LONGMANS, GREEN AND CO.

New York · London · Toronto

LONGMANS, GREEN AND CO., INC.
55 FIFTH AVENUE, NEW YORK 3

LONGMANS, GREEN AND CO. LTD.
6 & 7 CLIFFORD STREET, LONDON W I

LONGMANS, GREEN AND CO.
20 CRANFIELD ROAD, TORONTO 16

VENTURE INTO DARKNESS

PUBLISHED SIMULTANEOUSLY IN THE DOMINION OF CANADA BY
LONGMANS, GREEN AND CO., TORONTO

FIRST EDITION MARCH, 1955
REPRINTED MARCH, 1955

LIBRARY OF CONGRESS CATALOG CARD NUMBER 55-7205

Printed in the United States of America

VAN REES PRESS • NEW YORK

Dedicated
to
My Husband

EARLE TISDALE HOBART

without whom the novel
could not have been written

I saw the struggle
Of darkness against darkness. Within the room
It turned and turned, dived downward. Then I saw
How order might—if chaos wished—become:
And saw the darkness crush upon itself,
Contracting powerfully; it was as if
It killed itself, slowly: and with much pain.
Pain. The scene was pain, and nothing but pain.
What else, when chaos draws all forces inward
To shape a single leaf? . . .

From "The Room" * by Conrad Aiken

* From *Collected Poems*, Oxford University Press, Inc., New York. Copyright 1930, by Conrad Aiken.

Foreword

VENTURE INTO DARKNESS is a novel based on my own and others' experiences in China. I have attempted to present the facts in such a manner as to protect the friends who have so generously contributed of their own and their families' experiences. For the purposes of the story it has occasionally been necessary to telescope events, to take small liberties with the topography of the country, making the hills higher or lower and the valleys wider or narrower. But important as it is that the events portrayed in this book should be true, they are only the framework for the story of the struggle of man's spirit to survive the onslaught of Communist materialism.

Venture Into Darkness

Chapter 1

THE FREIGHTER, *Refuge*, HAD abandoned the direct route it usually took from Nagasaki to Hong Kong and was standing well out to sea in order to skirt a typhoon moving southeast down the coast of China, but even on the periphery of the hurricane the wind began slapping the vessel with seventy-five-mile-an-hour velocity. As the swell increased and the waves, topped with foam, began to pour over the now dangerously slanting deck, the captain faced his ship into the wind.

Down in his cabin David Conway, the ship's only passenger, took the belt of his dressing gown and tied himself into his bunk just in time to avoid being tossed and bruised as the sturdy but small craft plunged down the slope of one wave and was hurled upward on the steep incline of the next. Torrents of rain swept over the heavy glass porthole. Dishes in the nearby pantry fell to the floor with a crash. His suitcase and bags thumped against each other, raced wildly across the floor of the cabin. The wind twanged the ship's rigging. The bulkheads and iron doors leading to the engine room gave off creaks and grating sounds.

Night came. The fury of the storm drove from David Conway's mind the struggle which for many months had raged within him. Released from his own struggle, he gloated over the titanic struggle of the ship. With triumphant joy he felt the power of the vessel beneath him when, lying flat on his back in his bunk, he was stood all but erect each time the ship slid down the side of a wave, stood almost on his head when it climbed upwards. He revelled in the ship's power, mistaking it for his own. Man against catastrophe and man winning.

It was only when the typhoon had spent its force and the freighter stood to its original course, combatting nothing more than a heavy sea, and arrival in Hong Kong was only a few hours away, that he lost his exaltation. Leaning on the deck's rail, he nervously smoked one cigarette after another. Often he raised his binoculars, seeking the first glimpse of the coastline of China. He longed, yet dreaded to see it. When at last it appeared merely a wavering jagged line in the distance, he felt choked with the emotion of recognition.

Beyond that faintly discerned mountainous coast lay China, the country he knew better than his own. In memory he saw Southern China, its narrow and wide green valleys—green stretches seen through gossamer like rain—the cool green of bamboos, the dark green of mulberry trees, thick-leaved evergreen tea shrubs tipped in the spring with jade-green buds, rice paddies pricked with bright-green spears. Such was the backdrop of his adult years.

And he saw China's northern plains—the red-brown earth, the air in the fall made golden by the sun shining upon innumerable particles of dust sifting through it, red-brown heads of giant millet waving in the wind, the century-old roads, their ruts looking like indented railway ties dug deep by time into the sun-saturated brown plain. To this scene he had been born.

And the rivers—one by one they appeared to him. The Yellow River. In late years he had seen it so often from an airplane its old dried-up tributaries and swollen new ones, like the veins on an old man's hand, standing forth on the brown plain. The Yangtse, cutting its way through the heart of China, four thousand miles to the sea. Between cliffs, black masses which rose straight up for hundreds of feet, the tawny waters of the upper river in the summer swept in whirlpools, in races, in rapids, now in the autumn were dwindling away to the winter levels.

And China's cities—Hong Kong . . . no, he would not think of it, nor of Shanghai, but of Peking where he had spent his childhood, to him the most beautiful city in the world. Yes, and one of the most poverty ridden, but beautiful even in its poverty.

Time whirled around him, devoid of direction. The present was a vacuum. The past and the future girdled it as the circular winds had girdled the eye of the typhoon: his childhood spent among these people, he, with them, carried along on the stream of life; that stream then placid, now in flux, had tossed him carelessly to one side. Lonely and resentful he paced the deck.

Wanglow lighthouse, evidence that Hong Kong island was near, stood forth glaring white on its rock, but the towering top of the mountain island of Hong Kong was hidden in misty clouds. Only its headland was revealed: houses set among green, then an army camp, then a jumbled mass of refugee huts clambering up the mountainside. At last the freighter steamed through the Narrows. The mainland of China lay on the right, a cluster of junks on the left filled one of Hong Kong's many little bays. They passed into wider waters. The sun was going down. Too late for harbor inspection, they dropped anchor just off the strip of China's mainland leased to Britain many years ago. Opposite lay the city of Hong Kong stretched along the shelflike base of the island, its business center still in the distance —an island stronghold, proud possession, special pride of England, the last dim window through which the West could see, faintly visible, Communist China.

Suddenly, frighteningly clear to him was his own memory of the swift downsweep of China into the disaster of communism. He must not think of it. He needed all his energies for the undertaking which had brought him on this hazardous journey to this last foothold of the West existing precariously on this island at the tip of China's mainland, overlooked by islands fortified by Communist

4

China, crowded with refugees whose loyalty none could predict in time of crisis.

With dramatic suddenness the clouds were swept away. His eyes travelled from the harbor to the closely packed waterfront and up the shrub-covered slopes of the mountain. Tall white buildings stood out starkly from the mountainside, topped the peak. For a moment he was angry. It was a Hong Kong robbed of the green fastness— Hong Kong as he had seen it first as a boy. Then his anger was swallowed up in admiration. The stark white buildings were the proud answer of the British to defeat by the Japanese. Here a few years after the destruction meted out to them by the Japanese, the intrepid British, oblivious to the threat of Communist China, had re-created the city and this port. All around him in the harbor were the ships and war vessels of many nations. Viewing this city literally risen out of its own ashes, he felt a renewal of faith in himself. He, too, could win against catastrophe and win here.

"Well, do you think this place has anything to offer you?" Startled out of his absorption, Conway swung around to face the captain. Except for a few words exchanged between them over the delay caused by the storm, the captain had had no conversation with his passenger. The typhoon which had threatened to engulf them had kept him on the bridge a good deal of the time since they had left Nagasaki.

David had purposely avoided the captain, who impressed him as an inquisitive sort of person. Insignificant looking, he undoubtedly compensated for it by an importance he imagined he gained by retailing gossip collected from his passengers. He was like a drawing a child would make of a man—round head, round trunk, with two sticklike legs attached. Nervous and anxious not to reveal anything about himself, David parried the little man's question by asking, "What does Hong Kong have to offer *anyone* these days?"

"You mean it did once?" The captain rocked back on his heels the better to survey his passenger. "So you're not new to the East?" He was surprised. He rarely missed picking out a tourist. Certainly this American—somewhere between forty-five and fifty, he'd say—gave the impression of being a prosperous businessman on vacation. The twitch of his left eyelid indicated that he needed one. Tourist or not, he was prosperous. Everything about him looked expensive. His brown sports coat and slacks were well cut, his English brogues looked custom-made, his tie in shades of brown obviously was hand-blocked. "In business out here?" asked the captain.

Stupid, thought Conway, to have given himself away. The plane on which he had flown from San Francisco he had left at Nagasaki and had taken passage on the tramp so that his entrance into Hong Kong would be as inconspicuous as possible—obscurity fitted the mission on which he was embarked. But now that he had by those fatal words "these days" declared himself to be an old-timer to a man who undoubtedly enjoyed talking in the bars of Hong Kong, he must not appear secretive about his past. That would play into the captain's hands—give him a story to recount.

"I was in banking in Shanghai before I retired—in ship-

6

ping on the Yangtse before that," said David. "I haven't
been in Hong Kong for many years. I took passage on your
freighter thinking to get a little rest. I'm going south after
a glimpse of old friends here. Hong Kong is still a smug-
gler's haven, I suppose," he added, with the intention of
diverting the captain's attention.

"And how! Gold, for instance. Fantastic. Gold bullion
flown out to Macao. Bullion is legitimate business there,
but it's not legitimate in Hong Kong, although Hong Kong
has its own legalized gold exchange. Doesn't make sense,
does it? About two hundred thousand ounces of gold bullion get into Hong Kong illegally every month nowadays.
Fishing boats hide it under the fish. As there are about a
thousand of them, it's impossible to search them all. Border
patrols and custom sleuths can't keep up with the traffic."

"I suppose the Chinese Reds get hold of some of it."

"And how! There's a Communist clique operating
here," the captain answered, pleased to have an old-timer
ask him a question. "Didn't take them long to discover the
possibilities of the Hong Kong exchange market either.
Who's to stop them playing the free enterprise game here?"
he demanded. "They cash in handsomely on exchange.
Look at their Bank of China on the Bund. It's that tall
white building a story higher than the Bank of Hong
Kong next to it. If you haven't been here for some time,
that's new to you, too."

"Took money to build that Communist bank," said
David.

"There are plenty of ways to get it besides gold exchange. There's opium. Some say the Korean War is being

7

financed on opium smuggled out of China into Macao and Hong Kong, and shipped to the U.S.A."

"British don't stop it?"

"Can't. About as much chance as keeping water in a colander. Bays, inlets all around the island. Might as well try to keep sand from dribbling out between the fingers. That's why I say Hong Kong and Macao have nothing to fear from Red China. They're the nostrils through which China breathes. Reds too smart to stop up even one nostril."

"About it, I guess," said David.

"By the way, when did you leave Shanghai?" asked the captain.

"Let's see—late nineteen-forty-nine," David answered.

"Did you have any trouble getting out? I understand foreigners in key businesses had to get men from home to take their places before the Commies would let them go. Hostages held for money is what it amounted to, didn't it. You don't fight in Korea without a lot of money. A bankrupt country like China has to get it somewhere. Guess those stand-ins are taking the punishment now. Nobody was fool enough to return, once he got out."

"The substitutes were told the chances they were taking. And they were given huge salaries, I understand," Conway answered.

"Yes, I know—hard-bitten old China hands—most of them. They thought they were a match for any Chinese, but they found the Commies were a new breed of cats. It's tough on them just the same to be thrown into prison and held for enormous ransoms. Don't you think so?" asked the captain.

8

"I suppose so. How about a drink now that you're in port." Conway spoke casually enough, but the captain noticed with some interest how violently the man's left eyelid was twitching. Wonder what his story really is? Everyone who has ever lived out here has a story, he mused as he led the way to the freighter's dining saloon.

Over their drinks David tried again to change the subject. "Have the Chinese recovered from the last inflation Chiang Kai-shek's men brought about?" he asked. "It certainly was a mean trick raising the price on that gold loan the U.S. made for the purpose of stabilizing the currency. At the time we did what we could for our clients."—Indeed, the Chen family on whom David was depending for his present undertaking was one of them. It had been saved from bankruptcy by David's intercession at the bank.— "The Reds struck them a second blow when they confiscated the land. Most of the wealthy had their assets in land. Lucky, I suppose, if they reached Hong Kong with enough to live on."

"You'll see for yourself when you get ashore. Lots of poverty among the Chinese. Lots of wealth, too, even among the refugees. I don't know. Sometimes I think Chinese businessmen could survive any disaster. They're smart," said the captain. "But getting back to those hostages. Some of the companies paid a fantastic ransom to get them released, so it's rumored. Did you hear anything in America about how much the companies paid before the U.S. government cracked down on sending money into China?"

"That was kept pretty secret." Conway fell into a

9

moody silence. Was there no escape from this man's prodding over what men did to get substitutes?

Finally the captain rose. "I'm turning in." He was tired.
He had lost interest in this fellow who was undoubtedly
fearful of some disclosure. Maybe it was only that he had
had his nerves all shot up when the Japanese came in to
Shanghai. Those poor devils, never wanted to talk about
what happened to them. But he couldn't so easily dismiss
his passenger. There was something about him he could
not make out. His face was a mixture of strength and weakness—his features were clean cut, and yet the total effect
was a kind of blurring—the mouth, which once must have
been firm, was soft but unyielding. Still there was about
him the air of a man used to authority. When he was at sea
again, thought the captain, he'd try to work it out. It was
his entertainment on long voyages to write out the fates of
his passengers as he imagined them to be.

After his interrogator had left, David Conway went
back to the deck, determined to fix his attention on the
spectacle of the Hong Kong night—the window-lighted
mountain towering over the harbor shimmering with
lights on ships, junks and ferries—a scene both beautiful
and reassuring—a kind of beacon, this island, to guide white
men shipwrecked by the East, *in* the East, automatically
David corrected the language of his thoughts. Everything
would work out when he saw Chen. But he could not thus
easily dispel the spectre which had haunted him for many
months and to which the captain had given substance.
What right had the captain, safe on his ship, to pass judgment on the decisions of men struggling to extricate them-

selves and their companies from the Communists? It was common practice to get a stand-in, angrily David argued with himself, only to have that justification yanked from him. The man who had replaced him had not been a hard-bitten old China hand such as most foreign concerns had succeeded in getting, men willing to take risks because of the enormous salaries offered them, which would make them independent for life, believing that they could depend on their knowledge of the Chinese to keep them from offending the Reds during the time they were training Chinese to do their work.

Everyone believed once the Reds no longer needed foreign experts they would be free to leave. Certainly David had thought so when he had allowed Paul Damon to be his substitute. And it was to save his marriage that he had sacrificed Paul Damon on the altar of his own happiness. Sacrifice should be for a noble end . . . not a man's life given to save the tawdry marriage of Miriam and David Conway. What had he expected . . . that the blood of their scapegoat would cleanse Miriam and himself? Nonsense. Damon's blood was not on his hands. Damon wasn't dead. He was simply under house arrest.

Remorse, justification, remorse, round and round. Hour after hour David paced up and down. Gradually the harbor darkened. The brightly lighted ferries plied less frequently from mainland to island, from island to mainland. One by one the lights in the portholes of ships and war vessels went out; those on the decks were dimmed. The lights in the houses on the towering island went out. There remained only the yellow glow of the street lamps along the twisting roads leading up the mountain, lost finally in the night fog which had settled over the peak.

Round and round—justification. He never would have cabled Paul Damon the message he had, had it not been for Charlie Burton. It was he who had made it necessary for David to act promptly.

The last winter before the Reds had taken over Shanghai had been the most recklessly gay season the International Settlement had ever put on; love affairs flourished, conventional, lightheartedly flirtatious, wantonly abandoned, as both men and women sought to get something final from life before catastrophe, possibly death, overtook them. The charming Charlie, recently divorced, at first had carried on nothing more than a flirtation with Miriam—so Miriam had said. "He makes me feel young and sought after."

"I don't, I suppose?" David questioned.

"We've been married a long time, David, and not too successfully. I haven't forgotten what happened . . ."

"You mean—"

"You know what I mean."

"You haven't any right to hold that against me. The Japanese didn't feed us in the camps. You were away. Thank God I got you out in time. That Russian woman brought me food."

"And you gave her the kind of payment she wanted. It's my turn now," she had retorted with a bitter laugh. "I can manage Charlie. Just don't nag at me and everything will be all right."

But she hadn't been able to manage Charlie, or herself, either. The inevitable moment had come when she had

12

asked David for a divorce. He had begged her to wait. "It's the strain we're all under, not knowing when or if the Reds will take over. Go home, Miriam, live a normal life. I'll give you all the money you want. Go to the best dress-makers in New York. Buy all the smart clothes you want. Have a good time. You've lots of friends. I'll resign and come home as soon as the bank can make other arrangements. Give me a chance."

The bank had not accepted his resignation; instead it had suggested he take a vacation—when order was established in China and he was rested he might wish to go back. Both he and Miriam liked the plan, for they had grown accustomed to Shanghai's easy life. But before the home bank had completed their arrangements for his vacation, the Communists had taken over not only Shanghai but all the rest of China. Almost immediately they had made the rule that no foreign businessman could leave China without securing a substitute. The bank seemed unable to find any man who wanted the once-coveted position. One morning, several months after Miriam had left, Charlie had come into the bank ostensibly to say goodbye; but really to gloat, David felt. "My company has secured an old China hand to take my place. I'm flying home. I'll be in New York within a week. Wish me luck," he said.

David knew what Charlie meant by luck. He would be seeing Miriam within a few days—undoubtedly he would win her, hands down.

David thought he had carried it off pretty well. He had said quite casually, "Congratulations." Then he had rung

13

for his secretary to bring him his mail, saying, "Pardon me, won't you, we poor fellows who are left have to work." He wasn't going to let this cad think he was disturbed. When Charlie had gone, David searched through the pile of mail for a letter from Miriam. There was none. He opened one from the home bank. Nothing to help him in that—only the old gag about they hoped to relieve him soon. They'd been saying that for months. Wearily he picked up an envelope bearing the letterhead of another bank, opened it, glanced down the two paragraphs of the letter. It read—

"Dear Mr. Conway:
"Pardon me, a total stranger, for my presumption in writing you. I am taking this liberty because my decision involves us both. I hold a position in the foreign exchange department in this bank. Your bank has made me what seems to be a very flattering offer to act as your relief while you are on vacation. Although it involves giving up my present position for a temporary one, I feel the practical experience in handling exchange in a foreign country would be invaluable to me on my return.
"Knowing nothing of China except what I read in the papers, I consulted an old friend of the family who many years ago lived in China as to what the conditions would be under the Communists. Because of his long absence from China he felt unable to advise me. He suggested I write you. He said he had known your father years ago. You, he understood, had been brought up in China. That fact coupled with your experience in the China of today should mean you would be able to tell me how worthwhile the six months would be to me. I am

prepared to leave immediately if you so advise. Will you kindly cable me at my home address?"

Signed
Paul Damon"

Why should David's father be thrust into the foreground at this time? Why should he with his unrealistic criterion of goodness stand in his son's way at a time when, in the foreign communities like Shanghai, a man became expendable if he did not fight for his own rights? The peccadilloes of ethics were no longer possible. David wasn't going to have his wife snatched away from him without a fight. No man would. He wanted her... savagely... Miriam, dainty, elusive, never quite his although he had already paid a high price for her.

He wrote out a cable. "Experience excellent." Probably Damon was an older man who never before had had a good opportunity to show what he could do. Promotion in any bank was slow. This will be *his* break as well as *mine*. Thus David justified his cable.

His cable to Miriam read, "Relief coming. Be with you very soon. All my love. David."

After he had sent the two messages, he wrote out another to a New York florist ordering flowers to be delivered to Miriam each evening. He'd show Charlie what he could do.

A cable from Damon arrived promptly, saying that he'd be in Shanghai in just a week! David cabled Miriam, telling her of their good fortune.

Two days before he was expected, Damon walked into

15

David's office. "I'm Paul Damon. I caught an earlier plane," he explained, holding out his hand with engaging frankness.

He was tall and slender, the way a young man is slender. He *was* a young man and as simple, it flashed through David's mind, as his own father must have been when he first came to China. His father had survived, why shouldn't Damon? But this was a different China. Intimidation, treachery, deception were the norm, not the exception, in it now. The China of his father's day with its ideal of the superior man of right conduct could not be counted on any longer.

"I'm not a spectre."

"No, no, you're very much flesh and blood," said David. "I was expecting an older man."

"You think I won't do?"

"Yes, yes, of course. The day has gone by in China when it was the custom for young men to stand aside for their elders." Really there was nothing he could do about it, David told himself. The bank had made the arrangements. It was not his place to interfere. Besides, the man had given up his former position.

Damon was quick to learn the intricacies of local exchange rates, which were still fluctuating so rapidly as to make the problem of remittances a matter of continuous readjustment. This didn't seem to bother him. "It seems to be far better than it was under the Kuomintang," he kept saying. "I can see plenty of evidence of further improvement. They've already brought a lot of rice and coal in to help stabilize the currency. I think they'll have it in hand in

16

the near future. Even now you don't have to cart money around in wheelbarrows only to have to send a second wheelbarrow after the first because the exchange had gone up before arrival. Isn't that what you said you had to do a few months ago?"

But it proved far more difficult than David had expected to get Damon to grasp the contradictory viewpoints of old and new China. David remembered how he had struggled to dig up from the very centers of his being the understanding he possessed of the intricate and complicated personalities of the Chinese, and then to put this intuitive knowledge of his into words which would convey to Paul Damon the patience involved in living among and working with an Oriental people suddenly imbued with the successes and excesses of revolution.

Again and again he had drawn upon his store of knowledge to give Damon the insight he would need to negotiate with the new government over banking matters, also how to manage the problems arising over employees under the rapidly growing rules laid down by the Reds for every activity both public and personal. Each day there seemed to be a new regulation. Every effort he could make David had made until he was satisfied that Damon had a fair working knowledge of the mentality of the Chinese Reds with whom he would be dealing. The Chinese were clever, astute businessmen; however, human relations as understood by them were always a factor in negotiations. David still believed that even with the Communists the personal relationships could be established. There lay the ground-

17

work for any eventual adjustments which might have to be made between the Reds and the foreign banks.

In one of their last conversations David had said, "You know, Paul, that even in these changing times I lay great stress on human relations, which have been the basis of Chinese civilization for centuries. Friendship is an art with them. If you forget all the rest I have said, you'll be all right if you remember that. Make friends wherever you can—high or low."

"It's more important, I take it, than understanding exchange if I'm to survive," had been Damon's reply.

"I've not meant to discourage you," David hastened to say.

"Oh no," Damon had replied. "On the contrary, you've taught me a surprising amount in a very short time. I was certainly green when I arrived." After a pause, he added a little diffidently, "Would you mind calling up my wife when you get in? Tell her everything is fine. She will believe it if she hears it from you."

"You didn't tell me you were married!"

"It's all right, isn't it? It's perfectly legal." Damon had then taken a leather folder from his pocket, opened it and handed it to David, saying, "I've even got a daughter."

David stared at the two in the photograph, so alike—oval faces, large black eyes, trusting expression, as trusting in the woman as in the child. And then, in a voice the overtones of which he had resented, Damon had asked, "You don't mind guaranteeing my safety, do you? It will keep my wife from worrying."

"You're safe, Damon, if you keep your wits about you.

That's up to you," he had answered coldly. Why should the man ask him to guarantee his safety? The Reds had done nothing at that time to indicate that a foreigner was in danger. How could David know that Damon would be put under house arrest? Justification, remorse. He had not escaped them by coming to Hong Kong. He hurried along the deck of the freighter and down to his cabin. The bottle containing the sedative which his doctor had given him stood on the narrow shelf above the wash basin. He took the carafe from its socket, poured water into a glass, shook two tablets into it. While they were dissolving he undressed. With trembling hands, he raised the glass and drank the contents, then waited for sleep, but sleep did not come. Instead, the memory of the day when he had turned over the bank to Damon, the memory of the contempt in the eyes of the leader of the Chinese Reds who was arranging for the transfer. Was it contempt for him, or for Damon? "Under the capitalist system you give responsibility very early," the Chinese had said in a cultivated Oxford voice.

"In order that there may be rapport between us, since you, too, are young and carry heavy responsibilities," David had answered in a tone as suave as the other had used.

The night before he had left for America, he had made one more effort, the last he could think of, to help Damon. "I asked the amah to come in," he had said as the two men were sitting talking after dinner. "You haven't seen her yet. She rules behind the scenes. She'll rule you, too, but put up with it. She'll be the best friend you have. She brought me up. Her loyalty to me will be transferred to you."

How old amah had looked when she hobbled into the room, leaning on a cane he had given her. Never had he seen her so subdued. The actual ruler in his house for years, she had had the imperious bearing that becomes a ruler. But tonight he was startled to see that she looked both old and beaten. Suddenly it came to him that the greatest change in this city was in the old people. The ones you saw in the shops and along the street (the nicest old people in the world, he had always thought), their faces, once full of wisdom and kindliness, now like amah's seemed to have become shrunken and dispirited. And then, having offered Damon amah's friendship, David had had to withdraw it. "It's not that amah doesn't want to stay with you," he had explained. "It seems she has put all her savings into a piece of land. Her son has cared for it until now. The new government has a ruling that those who own land must work it."

"How can she!" Damon had exclaimed. "She's too crippled!"

Amah had turned toward David, talking rapidly.

"What does she say?" Damon had asked.

"Nothing to do about it. The new government says land is only made fertile by the sweat of the owner."

"I see," Damon had said. "I'm to be robbed of my best friend, it seems." Damon had then risen saying, "I think I'll send a letter to my wife by you if you'll be kind enough to take it."

Haunting David on the trip home were the faces of

Damon's wife and child—their eyes looking out so trustingly on a world that never had existed and never would. Such experiences as David and Miriam had been through bit deep into such trustfulness. Their marriage, if it survived, would be infinitely more of an accomplishment than the Damons'. Paul was one of those dull family men, scoffingly David told himself, trying to get rid of the faces of all three Damons.

As he left the plane at San Francisco a letter had been delivered to him. It was from Miriam, his welcome home. No! Telling him not to try to see her. "It's all over, David, don't let's tear each other to pieces again. I'm staying with Father and Mother until you give me my divorce. Please make it easy for me."

He wouldn't. On reaching New York, he had gone directly to the suburb where Miriam's parents lived. It was evening when he arrived. From across the street he watched the house. Miriam might come out and then he could see her alone, off guard. Then the door opened and Miriam *and* Charlie had come out. He felt smothered, thrust down into darkness of the spirit where passion, jealousy, writhing within him, seemed clasped around his throat, strangling him. Months passed in which he inhabited his own darkness—separate from his friends, separate from his work, for next day he had resigned from the bank.

Emerging slowly from this blackness he began to be haunted by Damon's last words, "Assure my wife that she has nothing to worry about." He called the bank hoping to find out that Damon was back. Instead, they had informed him his substitute was under house arrest. David

21

had immediately offered to go back and relieve him, but it was too late. That Damon would be shut into the country and he shut out was a turn of events he had not foreseen. In vain the bank had offered money for Damon's release only to have new but unexplained charges brought against him. Then the American government had prohibited any money's being sent to China to ransom Americans. The bank could do nothing more.

The antagonism the Chinese Reds already felt toward America for aiding Chiang Kai-shek was raised to an obsession at the outbreak of the Korean War. House arrest, imprisonment were indiscriminately meted out to Americans, missionary and businessman alike. Nationals of other countries were left free—although not allowed to leave the country. Was it Damon's ignorance of Chinese ways which made them refuse the very substantial ransom earlier offered them by the bank? David could not rid himself of this possibility.

One morning David had received a telephone call from the bank, saying the president would like to see him. As he entered the president's private office a young woman had risen and faced him. It was Mrs. Damon. But her eyes no longer held that expression of naive trust they had held in the picture. Now she, too, had suffered. She, too, had been deprived of her mate—all that that meant.

"I've been explaining to Mrs. Damon that we are doing all we can, that everything is now in the hands of the State Department," the president had told him, "but she is not satisfied. She asked to see you."

"With your understanding of the Chinese, surely you

can do something. Paul wrote that your wisdom in dealing with them was extraordinary." As she spoke Mrs. Damon looked straight at David. Her eyes accused him. He shook his head. Without a word she rose and left. When an hour later, after talking over every angle of the situation with the president, he left the bank, he found her outside, obviously waiting for him. "Certainly there is something you can do. Not officially of course, but personally," she demanded.

"You look tired," he had answered. "There's a quiet place near here where we can get a cup of coffee and I can explain that it's impossible to do anything now." For a long time they had sat in the shop, he trying to explain, she refusing every explanation. Finally in exasperation he had said, "You have no knowledge of the situation. Why do you keep insisting that you know what should be done?"

"Paul didn't know the situation either but you thought him capable of managing the bank. Am I more ignorant than he?" she retorted. Again her eyes accused him.

Overcome by his own guilt he had promised her that he would attempt the impossible—go to Hong Kong and secretly negotiate for her husband's release. "I have a Chinese friend . . . he might be able to arrange personally to ransom your husband where officially the bank has failed. You understand I have no legal right to do this."

"You will need money?" she asked, ignoring his last remarks.

"No," he answered.

Well, he was fulfilling his promise. Tomorrow he would

be learning what his Chinese friends had been able to arrange—if anything. David had been disturbed when, on reaching Japan, he had received a letter telling him that the elder Chen, the member of the family to whom he stood in the relationship of friend, was dead. The son, the author of the letter, had graciously offered David what help he could, but David was concerned as to whether a son would feel bound by inherited obligations of friendship. Then there flashed through David's mind the strange history of this family. In reality his dead friend, the elder Chen, had no son to represent him. Death had wiped out a generation—a special tragedy in a Chinese family. An epidemic had taken Chen's children. As his lineal descendant he had adopted his brother's second son. It was this man, this adopted son, to whom David must now appeal for help.

David rose and gulped down another sleeping tablet.

Chapter 2

HE WAS AWAKENED BY THE
throbbing of the ship's engines. It was daylight. The night
was a blank. No movements on the freighter had penetrated his heavy sleep. Neither had the presence of Paul
Damon or Miriam; the drug had done its merciful best,
erasing their troubling images. With none of the nervous
tension with which he had undressed the night before,
David dressed, choosing a thin, tropical suit, for the morning was warm and sticky. He went on deck to watch the
freighter move up the harbor. The sun, shining through
breaks in the clouds which hung around the mountain's
peaks, lay upon the roofs of houses in a narrow valley. Like

25

a stream they seemed to flow down the mountainside. Sun lay over the harbor. It touched the brass fittings on nearby war vessels; it sparkled on the white wake of ferries moving toward and away from the city.

The freighter tied up to a buoy abreast of the city's center. At sight of David standing at the rail several sampan men began clamoring to take him ashore. A woman in shining black trousers, her top garment open and swinging, fought for the coveted place at the foot of the gangway, alternately shouting up to him and cursing the other sampan owners crowding in on her. The East in all its normal raucous, brawling vitality gave David, the old China hand, an invigorating, if false, sense of the greater dignity of the white man and his ability to control the East. With a sense of mastery of himself he had not had for a very long time, he went down to breakfast. The saloon was empty. He ate leisurely.

As he finished his breakfast he felt the first faint sense of anxiety. Surely by now he should have had a message from Banker Chen. He was about to leave the saloon, when a young Chinese wearing a lightweight, fawn-colored suit, entered the saloon and came leisurely toward him. "Are you not Mr. Conway?" he asked, with a polite bow slightly reminiscent of the elaborate bow of an older generation. "I am Chen Mu San. Undoubtedly you don't remember the boy you met years ago."

"Mu San, of course," said Conway, although for a moment the name meant nothing to him. Now he remembered the first time he had heard it—a New Year's Day when the senior Chen had come with the male members

26

of his family to make the traditional New Year courtesy call. Mu San, the youngest of the three grandsons, year after year until he had gone to Peking for his studies in the university, had dutifully accompanied his elders on the yearly courtesy call although it was not difficult to detect in the young man a half-concealed unwillingness to do so. There was no sign of such unwillingness this morning.

"My father wished me to express his concern that he could not meet you." Mu San spoke with engaging frankness. "He wishes the day to be a happy one for you. I thought we'd drive around a bit if you are interested in what's happened here."

Happy, thought David, he knows I'm not here to play. And this sending of a substitute, the youngest member of the family! Could it be that Mu San's father had chosen this indirect method of informing David that he felt no obligation to aid him? But it couldn't be. David knew Mu San's father well. Often he had represented the family on banking matters. He had always been meticulous in fulfilling obligations undertaken by the head of the family. Family responsibility, David believed, strongly motivated all his actions. As David had come to the family's rescue in a time of great emergency, in fact by so doing saving the family fortune, surely this man steeped in the Chinese responsibility to personal relationships would not brush David's request aside or bring him so far for no purpose. What, then, was the meaning of this nonappearance of the head of the family? There was an interpretation which was in accordance with the best Chinese tradition—not to appear would be a way of saving the face of a friend who asked something that it has proved impossible to grant. Could it be that the negotiations for Paul Damon's freedom had broken down and thus indirectly David was being informed of the failure? Trained through a lifetime to find a second meaning in such a statement as young Chen had just made, David for a moment lost hope.

"There's a restaurant in the old part of the city where we can get a good luncheon," he heard young Chen say. "Later in the day my father has arranged for a small feast in your honor in one of the new restaurants overlooking the harbor. My father remembered you were very fond of some of our dishes. He ordered the meal himself before he left. But perhaps first I should ask if there are any friends here you would like to see."

"Only your father. I have come far to see him on an important matter," answered David, determined to find out where he stood.

"It is an honor that you regard my father to be trusted with your confidence," Mu San replied blandly as he stood aside to let David precede him down to a small launch at the foot of the gangway.

"Since there are no friends here you wish to see, suppose we drive around the island. My servant will take your bags to the hotel. Do you mind walking a half block to my car?"

"Not at all," David answered, letting go for the time being the troubling question of how to regard such stalling —for stalling it certainly was.

Mu San's delicate-boned hands lay lightly on the wheel as he maneuvered his car through the ordered traffic of rickshas, cars, crowds of foreigners and Chinese en route to their offices in downtown Hong Kong, then through the godown area where streams of coolies, unmindful seemingly of the advancing car, crossed the road from the great lighter junks to the warehouses, heavy loads at the ends of their carrying poles.

The splendidly built wide road began to mount, dipping and rising following the contours of the hills and valleys. With such a road it wouldn't take more than a couple of hours at the most to circle the ten-mile-long, five-mile-wide island. A great Daimler to accomplish the Lilliputian feat! It struck Conway as ridiculously tragic, these rich Chinese exiles putting on an empty show like this. Both men were silent.

When they came to the fishing village of Aberdeen, Mu San stopped, saying, "If you will pardon me I will do a small errand for my father." With that he went into a wayside temple, paused by a soothsayer sitting at the side of the fisherman's patron saint. While he was away, David walked along the waterfront watching the overflowing life on the junks. Women and children, whole families lived in the cabins at the stern. This was China as he knew it—and he loved it.

Deep Water Bay, Repulse, innumerable inlets, larger ones, small ones slipped by the fast-moving car. The words of the captain of the freighter came back to David, "like a sieve. The smugglers get out through the holes."

"That thin line over there is a Communist country—it's fortified," young Chen volunteered, waving his hand toward an island in the distance. "Incredible, isn't it? You'd think the British would feel insecure sitting right under the Red guns."

"Don't you think they do?" asked David.

"Isn't a Britisher always superior?" There was the slightest edge to the word "superior." "I mean to danger," young Chen added, but too late to disguise his real meaning. "You know, men were throwing dice for drinks in Singapore ten minutes before the Japanese crawled in through the jungle. The British go down wearing the old school tie—tradition, you know. In Stanley Prison during the Japanese occupation the layers of English society were maintained." He laughed lightly. "Pardon me, but it does amuse me, but only because the West has talked so much about democracy."

"There's something rather magnificent about the way the British have rebuilt this island, and given sanctuary to two million hard-pressed Chinese forced out of China," David replied. He thought of the hillside they had passed, with thousands of boxlike cement habitations housing refugees, yes, and of the Chen family living here under British protection.

With genuine frankness, it seemed, young Chen answered, "I'm sorry, it was rude of me to criticize the British before you and ungrateful, but you understand that we Chinese are bitter over British-owned Hong Kong—an old bitterness, as you know. Yet what would we do if we didn't have it to shelter us now? We are indeed grateful. Gratitude, as you know, with a Chinese, is a responsibility never side-stepped. I think side-stepped is the word you use."

Conway studied his companion. He seemed two persons:

many of his remarks were typical of young Chinese well known to David—the Western-educated student who felt personally humiliated by China's inferior position among the great nations and hit back on all occasions; other remarks he made were in the tradition of the Chinese gentleman who could not be jarred out of his exquisite politeness —remarks such as the elder Chen, David's old friend, would have made, gracious acknowledgment of the favor rendered him by a friend. In the past David would have taken Mu San's last remark as a sign that he might now mention the real nature of his visit. Yet he hesitated. How far should he go in divulging the nature of his business with this younger member of the family? Does he know of the offer of help already made me by his father? If so, why does he not mention it?

Mu San, increasing his speed, was heading back toward the city. "Forgive me. You must be hungry," he said with sudden concern. "It's well past noon."

Knowing that in a restaurant there would be little chance of talking privately, David decided to make Mu San take some stand. "Chen Mu San, when am I to see your father?" he asked.

"Oh, I had meant to come to that."

What in hell, thought David, why hadn't he spoken before? He's had plenty of time. What was young Chen's game anyway?

"I speak frankly," Mu San continued. "My father has confided in me the urgency of your errand and also has entrusted to me the carrying out of today's plans. It is, as you well know, a supremely difficult thing you have asked of him, but in his desire to discharge with honor the obligation to you, passed down to him from my grandfather, he has assumed the task."

David didn't like it that Mu San, although apparently willing to concede there was an obligation, at the same time hedged it about with the implication that he was asking a greater favor in return for a lesser one. David was again the wary Western businessman trained through years to find hidden meanings in Chinese negotiations. He had come here with the father's full knowledge of the issues involved. What was behind young Chen's effort to embarrass him—at least so it seemed to David.

"Confucius says—"

"Let's leave Confucius out of it," David retorted, angered out of the calmness he knew he should maintain. "I am here in response to a letter from your father. It seems only natural that I should see him."

Mu San's manner changed instantly. He was respectful and forthright. "If you had gone to my father's house directly from the ship, you might have been trailed. He wants you to be seen about town. He wants the impression to get out that you are merely passing through and that we are simply extending to you the hospitality my great grandfather, had he been living, would have extended to you. You are to see my father tonight."

"Very well," said David, "if that is the way your father wishes it." He did not add that he thought such a plan only made him more vulnerable to detection. He wondered if young Chen could be trying to throw him off base for some purpose of his own. Immediately David regretted that he had harbored such an unfounded suspicion. Were his nerves playing him false? So desperately in need of help, he asked himself, was his mind fogged by anxiety?

As the day went on, Conway's puzzlement over young Chen grew. Chen, the traditional Chinese, a cultivated gentleman, polite and meticulous in his traditional submission to his father, was repeatedly replaced by the Western-style youth who, under the pretense of Western frankness, was rude to his grandfather's and father's friend, a violation of one of Confucius' precepts—of right conduct. Under the guise of entertaining him, Mu San lost no opportunity to show David the evidences of Western imperialism. He knew every tragic exploitation of the East by the West. More and more as the day advanced he made use of such incidents to embarrass his father's friend.

Late in the afternoon, he drove his guest up the winding road to Victoria Peak. David, having decided it was better to wait until evening when he would see Mu San's father for any discussion of his errand, made an effort during the drive to ease his irritation by trying to recapture the wonder and delight of his first trip to "The Peak." A young boy had come from the cold north one winter, to this beautiful, fragrant mountain. In a sedan chair, hoisted on the shoulders of men, he had ridden up the steep roads, roads now winding and twisting in switchbacks which made possible this swift ascent by motor. The island was more beautiful then—banyan trees bordering the white roads lowered their branches to the ground, sent new roots down into the earth, making one tree a labyrinth of trees. The houses, set among tropical flowers and smooth lawns, their deep verandas supported by series of pillars, duplicating the arches of the banyans, had spoken to him of life lived luxuriously, even voluptuously. Ambition had awakened in him that day. It was then he had determined he would be rich. "What's happened to the banyan trees?" he asked.

"Progress," his companion answered. "Roots interfered with the water system. Trimmed back, controlled, British efficiency. These great apartment houses offend me but, as you are an American, I imagine you like them."

"On the contrary—" David began, then did not finish his sentence. To be sure these houses were unrelated to the mountain's contours. The stunted trees and wild greenery of the stony mountain were not tall enough to soften their bare white perpendicular surfaces. But these apartment houses, he knew, were practical, for they conserved land on this crowded island.

The road narrowed. Mu San stopped the car. "Suppose we walk a little farther. The mist is clearing. There's a magnificent view a little farther on." They rounded a curve in the mountain road. "There," he said softly.

No need for words now. For the first time David felt in harmony with the young Chinese as they stood silently looking at the beautiful scene. The mountain on which they stood sloped down to gray-blue waters. Across on the mainland a lofty range of mountains made a magnificent backdrop to the harbor and sea and the vast archipelago— peaked green islands—the tops of submerged mountains studding the harbor and sea.

Mu San waved his hand, exclaimed, "What a powerful

play could be written here with your Bible tale as a basis. Lay the scene on this mountaintop—let his Satanic majesty bring here a Christian man ... any Westerner, you, for instance, could personify the Christian man ... offer him all this lying at his feet in exchange for his soul. The tragedy is he accepts. I'm surprised the Reds haven't thought of it as a part of their propaganda. You know, they make use of the drama to teach."

This was the final insult, distorting the central truth of Christ's renunciation of the world. Angrily David started to speak, stopped. He dared not quarrel with young Chen, his only avenue of approach to the elder Chen, his only chance to rescue Paul Damon and redeem himself. Struggling for control, he turned from his companion and stared at the city below him. The island mountain on which it stood had been acquired by the British in a war over opium. Kowloon, the strip of mainland opposite, had been acquired later to protect the island. There was Macao on a tip of the mainland which he could not see, but he was certain young Chen was thinking of it, held for centuries by the Portuguese. And David knew, as did Chen, how the whole coastal area of China had been nibbled away by Western nations. America had never held any of China's land, David thought self-righteously, only to be confronted with the fact that America had partaken of the privileges for which other nations had fought. An overwhelming sense of the Western man's guilt held him silent and shaken —then he rallied his forces, gathered together in his mind the good the West had wrought in the East. All this young man had in comfort, ease, and modern education had come to him through the West! No such epidemic as had wiped out a generation in his family could happen now to the Chen family. The Chinese had learned to use the science of modern medicine through Western doctors, many of whom had given their lives in China's behalf. China's curse —devastating floods, in some regions at least—had been done away with forever because of the work of engineers like David's father, he who had given his life in service to China. "We have taken but we have given also. What about our Christian doctors, our teachers, our engineers?" David demanded, turning and facing Mu San.

"Forerunners of Western imperialism," snapped Mu San.

"What about Russian imperialism?" David asked.

"Well, what of it?" countered Mu San.

David sighed. No use talking to this resentful young man. He did not wish harmony between them. For some reason he wanted to believe the worst of the West. Then, born out of his long knowledge of the Chinese people, David caught a glimmer of what was upsetting Mu San. He had lost his foothold: he and his family were refugees, proud people, steeped in thousands of years of China's imperial grandeur, accepting asylum was too great a humiliation. Young Chen found relief in blaming on Western aggression his present tragic predicament as a refugee.

The sun set. The outlines of the islands and mainland grew softer in the gentler light. Soon the short twilight of the tropics gave place to darkness. Lights from a thousand different points on harbor and land sprang up. With no word spoken between them, they went back to the car and started down the mountain. Then this baffling young man made an unexplainable gesture toward harmony. He stopped near the Anglican Cathedral. "Would you care to go in?" he asked. And David was grateful. He had come here with his father on that first visit to the island. Then he had prayed; now he would pray—ask for a chance to save Damon, redeem himself. When he rose to leave he saw Mu San far back in the church, his head bowed!

The hours of tension and waiting were almost over. David had before him now only the feast spoken of earlier in the day, and then he would see his friend. Indeed, he was being honored, he thought, as young Chen led him to a half-curtained off corner of the restaurant and introduced him to the bankers and merchants gathered to meet him, all men of an older generation. Very elegant they were in their silk summer gowns, small satin skullcaps on their heads, narrow black satin slippers on their narrow feet. But despite their elegance they were bankers and merchants without banks and without shops, dispossessed by the Communists, dependent upon the mercy of Great Britain for survival.

Through the aperture left by the half-closed curtain, David glanced around the great room. At a table nearby sat a family—little children, young people smartly dressed and even an old lady wearing the old-fashioned black satin headband of the married woman. David wondered what she thought of a group of young women unchaperoned at the next table. A few years ago it would not have been proper for them to stray outside the women's quarters of the family home. They wore the long, straight gown of their people, so becoming to them. David knew from Miriam that only skillful tailors could give that chic, slender line. Evidently the Chinese gathered here were wealthy refugees from Shanghai. All in the room were richly dressed and they spoke the Shanghai dialect.

Not only they but the poor, the diseased, the harlots, the gamblers, the smugglers, cast out by the puritanical but godless Communists, had been given shelter on this over-crowded island. "Come unto me all ye that are weary and heavy laden" thought David—the last act of Chen's play was being enacted here on this island, even as the first had been, and with compassion.

Glancing at his host, he marvelled. Even in his Western clothes young Chen now definitely belonged to old China. With dignified humility he was ministering to his grand-father's and father's friends. With his chopsticks he lifted special morsels from the central dish, placed them in the bowl of the honored guest; he drank thimble-sized cups of warm wine with one guest after the other. For a time, warmed by the wine, the food, and the companionship, David was able to shut out the urgency of his errand.

Suddenly a tremendous explosion shook the building, rattled the dishes. Had the Reds attacked? Had they taken the island? The diners were on their feet. Some were sick, vomiting the rich food.

Then the proprietor stood among his guests. "Fang Sin! Fang Sin! Let your hearts be at rest!" he shouted. "An oxygen tank at the shipyards blew up." With as much nonchalance as they could muster, the diners sank back in their chairs.

One young woman at the nearby table took from a jeweled handbag a tiny silver mirror encrusted with jewels and carefully repaired her make-up. Young Chen stared fixedly at these elegantly clad young ladies. One, dressed in a pale-lavender gown with pearls closing the collar at her throat, returned Mu San's stare.

"Petals, just petals on a dying flower stalk," David heard young Chen murmur.

One course followed another, but at last the rice was brought. Young Chen now looked at the flushed faces around him with a hint of disdain, but his words were suave and in good Chinese tradition. "My father's friend is weary," he said at last. "If the honored guests will permit us, my humble self will drive the most honored guest for a little in the cool night air before he goes to his hotel. He must be rested for his journey tomorrow. Please excuse the miserable son of your unworthy host for leaving this honorable company, but it is on account of the august guest."

Chapter 3

THEY DROVE A SHORT DIS-
tance down the road from the restaurant, changed into a
smaller car. In it they skirted a narrow valley, ascended
steeper, narrower streets. The atmosphere of Hong Kong,
it seemed to David, had changed abruptly. He felt more at
home in this part of the island. Tall, narrow houses, such
as he remembered, rose steeply out of the pale moonlit
evening, their arched verandas, two stories high, framed
French windows, arched as were the verandas, most of
them lighted. Close to the car on either side retaining walls
held back the mountain.

Mu San negotiated a sharp turn. In the interim it took

him to shift gears for the still steeper climb, David caught a glimpse of a brilliantly lighted flight of steps leading up the mountain. At the sides of the steps vendor's trays were lighted by small lamps, naked bulbs were suspended over the counters of shops alongside. Signs in gold calligraphy hung down from the tall buildings. Crowds of Chinese in a multitude of colored garments, laughing and talking, were ascending and descending the steps. The car moved forward. David looked back. The slit which seemed to open on the China he knew was closed in by a steeper part of the road.

All at once to the right a gate in a retaining wall swung open and Mu San drove in and up a short steep grade to a wide terrace from the edge of which the mountain dropped away in dizzy suddenness. As they were getting out of the car another car drove in through the gate and a man in Chinese dress jumped out of it and came toward David, holding out his hand, a wholly Western act. "My apologies for not meeting you this morning. I hope my son has already made apology and explained to you that at the last moment an obstacle occurred in our arrangements to carry out what I so gladly have tried to arrange—our joint undertaking." Mr. Chen, for it was he, spoke in Chinese and the fast-flowing words and the genuineness of his apology removed the uncertainties so troubling to David all day.

With energetic steps Mr. Chen led the way toward a tall house standing far back on the terrace. At the door he stopped and bowed, begging David to enter first. When David refused, they entered the hall together, young Chen

41

following. Voices came from a room at the left. "My family," said Mr. Chen, "gathered to do you honor. My wife speaks no English," he explained, leading David to a middle-aged woman seated on a semicircular divan opposite the door. She was dressed in a sober gray Chinese gown and she sat stiffly on the divan, her hands folded in her lap. Her face gave no indication of pleasure or displeasure. David bowed, greeting her with Chinese formality. The room, he observed, was wholly modern, but not Mr. Chen's wife. The sons and their wives, the daughters and their husbands and children were introduced by Mr. Chen. The men, like their fathers, wore European dress; the girls wore their sheathlike Chinese gowns—so becoming to their slender physique.

Tea was brought, Mr. Chen asked about his friend's voyage, his family. Although with patience gained in his childhood David Conway answered the questions, then asked Mr. Chen and Mrs. Chen like ones in return—where their children had been educated, were they all married, had they sons and grandsons, were they all at home—these extra moments of waiting after the long suspense of the day seemed unbearable. This terrible Eastern politeness! Finally Mr. Chen arose. "Let us go to my father's apartment," he said, turning to his guest. "These old houses built on the side of the mountain have floors below as well as above. My father preferred the seclusion of the lower floor," he explained, leading David down a flight of steps at the end of the hall. "We can talk freely here."

The room they entered was lighted by an electric bulb hanging directly over a large Chinese table which stood in the middle of the room. On the table was a blue porcelain pen holder, erect in it a dozen pin-pointed writing brushes. Across the polished top of the table lay a piece of white paper with a few beautifully drawn characters on it. The walls were hung with scrolls, examples of the same fine calligraphy. "My father's work," Mr. Chen said with pride, stopping before one of them.

So the elder Chen had taken refuge in scholarship, like so many of the upper-class Chinese. While he waited for the Communist holocaust to burn itself out, thought David, he, like his ancestors in time of disorder, rested on the historian's words, "After the ebb, the flow."

"Here is his garden." For a moment after Mr. Chen switched off the light in the room David saw nothing but darkness, then through an open window he saw a small walled-in space, lighted dimly by a young moon. Against the white wall lay the shadowy branches of a tree. Above loomed the dark mass of the mountain. David remembered the elder Chen's garden in Shanghai, his trees reflected in still ponds—a quiet retreat. "My father, as you know, was a Taoist," said his son. "He spent much of his time here during his last days."

David's sense of haste and anxiety faded. It was as if the serene spirit of his friend still lingered here as his family believed—the months were not yet passed when his spirit would leave the earth he loved.

After a long pause, David's host switched on the light in the room and motioned David to be seated. According to ancient custom David demurred at taking the honored place. Finally he was seated in a chair on the left side of a small, square table, and Chen on the right. Like chairs and table, according to custom, were set against the opposite wall. A very old man brought them tea.

"It is a great honor to aid my father's friend—return in part the kindness you did for him. He never forgot it, nor do I."

"It was nothing," murmured Conway.

Then Mu San, who had not entered the room with them, came in and pulled up a chair in front of them, breaking the set pattern, the balanced arrangement of chairs and table. He had changed into a Chinese gown of black cotton, such as the Northern Chinese usually wear when travelling. "We had information only yesterday of a very grave nature concerning the man who relieved you," Mu San said, thus ending his father's slow Eastern approach to the matter that concerned David. "As you already know, Mr. Damon is under house arrest. We find that recently he has been accused of defrauding the government of money. This is regarded as a criminal offense, so the amount of money you offered for his release is not adequate for such an offense."

"How much do they want?"

"A half million—the amount they claim he embezzled."

"A half million! They know it's impossible!" cried David.

"That is why they ask it," the elder Chen spoke gravely, "but the situation is not hopeless. We are pretending to negotiate while we arrange for his escape. We have ways of entering and leaving the China mainland."

An underground? So the Chens, even the late head of

44

the family who seemingly had taken refuge in Taoism, and possibly even the men with whom David had feasted earlier in the evening were not as resigned to the new regime as they appeared to be, was David's first thought. Then the enormity of the undertaking struck him. "Free a Western man closely guarded for a criminal offense!" David exclaimed, turning to Mr. Chen. "I could not ask you to take such a risk."

"It is difficult, but it is possible. Even the Reds relax sometimes, and many still can be influenced by money. After all, they are Chinese." A faint suspicion of a smile hovered around the placid lips of the new head of the Chen family.

Again David protested, "I cannot accept."

"It is an obligation my family gladly assumes." These words were proudly spoken by Mr. Chen.

Although saving the Chen family from bankruptcy was a considerable service, David felt the proposed repayment, which might endanger Chen's whole family—since revenge could undoubtedly reach even into Hong Kong—was out of proportion to the debt. Now he understood Mu San better; more modern in his thinking than his father, he rightly objected to such a payment.

"You can trust us." Mr. Chen spoke with great dignity.

"Trust," said David, "has always existed between us. But if to save the man who is standing in my place I risk *your* family standing in my place, I but shift my debt from one shoulder to the other."

"That debt, if it occurs, can be settled later. We hope

45

it will not be incurred. Let us forget it for the present. The time is short."

"Let me explain the situation," Mu San put in. "This Damon, who came to China as your substitute, during the time he has been under house arrest has seen no one except his accusers and the coolie who once a day brings him food. He has not stood up well under the strain."

A flaw in the Westerner had made him break—was that the implication? David's irritation with Mu San returned. From childhood he had been accustomed to a certain sense of superiority in the Chinese, but it was the understandable superiority that highly educated men often feel toward those who are ignorant—in Chinese eyes Westerners were not cultured men. The foreigners had long met this attitude with the belief that Western science with its efficiency made the West superior to the East. Balance was kept by each recognizing his own dignity which the other respected, but young Chen's superiority was touched with scorn. Once again, as so often during the day, David wished he did not have to deal with this overbearing youth.

"Many have broken under the strain of imprisonment," said the elder Chen, thus softening his son's words. "And this man has received particularly harsh treatment. His kindness and courtesy had won for him many friends among the Chinese—he held meticulously to the Chinese concept of friendship. Such a man spoils the Communist propaganda that Americans bring only harm to China. They are the ones the Communists wish to break."

What have I done? thought David. It was I who drilled

Paul Damon in the art of Chinese friendship! "Has he been tortured?" he managed to ask.

"Not physically—at least so far. They have ways to break the mind. He shrinks in terror from the sight of a Chinese," the elder Chen answered.

David was too shocked to speak.

"My son and I have discussed the matter," Chen went on. "With your cooperation we believe we can bring this terrified one in safety to Hong Kong, where with kind treatment he will undoubtedly recover."

"How can I help?" asked David, recovering from his first shock.

"If he escapes, he will have to have someone who can quiet his fears, someone who speaks his own language."

Mu San again interrupted. "He understands very little Chinese. This, coupled with his fear of the Chinese, makes you a necessary part of our plans. Once we have rescued him we shall need you to handle him."

Two Americans to bring out of China instead of one! "Fantastic!" exclaimed Conway. He was not prepared to go to such lengths to help Paul Damon.

The two Chens waited. In the realm of personal relationships, such an act came within the Confucian code of right conduct—Damon had guaranteed his life for David's; now David must offer his in return.

"I must think. There are other responsibilities I have to consider," said David. And yet he knew that he had no responsibilities which outweighed this one. He had gone out of Miriam's life for the last time. He had no children—

47

such had been the agreement when he married Miriam. His parents were dead.

Empty of meaning as his life seemed just now, it was still precious to him and he saw no reason for surrendering it. For years he had lived in Shanghai's competitive world of business and society. He and Miriam had fought for their place in both; the struggle had even entered into their personal lives, each trying to get the utmost out of the other. Those years informed his thinking now. Remorseful though he was over his part in Paul Damon's tragic situation, he could not believe it was demanded of him that he should risk his own life to save Paul's. David was in no doubt about what the Reds would do to him if they caught him entering the country without their permission. They would treat him as a spy. Surely he was not Paul Damon's keeper! Surely even Mrs. Damon would not expect such a sacrifice.

And then the two Chinese waiting for his answer placed their boundaries around him. Drilled in childhood to the Chinese code of right conduct, David could not extricate himself from it now. Further entangling him was the teaching of his parents, in whom honor was a priceless thing. East and West united to propel him out of his years of self-interest to a level of spiritual maturity where he was able to accept his responsibilities for Paul Damon's plight. "Tell me the details. If it seems practical to get the two of us out, I will go," he said in a voice he did not recognize as his own.

"I have arranged for a junk to leave late tonight with a cargo. That is what detained me today. Getting cargo out

48

of Hong Kong is difficult, but it can, with care, be arranged. Piracy is an old business on this coast, as you know. The pirates are against the Communists. We have found it safe to work with them in getting people out of China," said Mr. Chen.

There flashed through David's weary mind the words of the captain on the freighter, "Like a sieve!" The island's little inlets and bays provided innumerable outlets for smugglers. "And after I land?" he asked.

"We shall be in the hands of the underground. They will get us to Shanghai."

"Us?"

"I shall go with you," said Mu San, "as far as Shanghai."

"I cannot accept so great a sacrifice."

Mu San shrugged. "There is a member of the family also to be rescued."

"We have had word where Third Uncle is hiding," Mr. Chen explained. "It is a family responsibility to bring him safely to Hong Kong."

"Do we not need time to prepare?" asked David, searching his mind for some acceptable excuse. Often in his life he had longed to be tall like his father. If only he were, he thought, he could use his height as an excuse. But, average in height, he knew that with his dark-brown eyes and dark hair disguise was possible.

"The Reds may decide to execute Damon any day if our negotiations break down," he heard Mr. Chen say. "We'll keep them talking as long as we can."

"I can see we must not lose a moment," David answered after a pause.

For an hour they discussed every phase of the undertaking. David's hair must be dyed. He would be provided with Chinese clothes, a cap to pull down over his eyes. When they reached Shanghai he would be hidden until the time came when some member of the underground could knock out the guards and rescue the prisoner. David must be on hand to quiet him if he should become violent. The Chens believed the journey out of China could be accomplished without too much danger. They might have to hide for a little. With luck the whole thing might be accomplished in a few weeks' time.

During the next hours David came to appreciate Mu San. It was he who suggested that David had better go in person to the hotel to get his luggage and say he was staying the night with a friend. "Then there will be no one to betray you later on. The Communists are everywhere. It is wiser to trust no one," Mu San explained. It was he who drove David to the hotel, and it was he who, after their return, arranged what belongings could be taken and what must be left behind—a few comforts for use on the junk, the bare necessities for the journey overland. "Only what we can put in our pockets and fasten to our belts when we leave, soap, your razor of course. You must be clean shaven all the time," young Chen explained, showing David to an upstairs room to which his luggage had already been brought.

Then, after providing David with the cotton trousers and Lenin jacket, the dictated garb for Communist China, Mu San left him, saying, "You won't need me for a little. I will now make my own preparations." He paused a moment at the door to add with traditional dignity, "If you will allow me now to quote Confucius, 'In quiet a man prepares for a journey.' " Quietly he shut the door behind him.

After leaving Conway, young Chen went back to his father. He found him still sitting where he and the foreigner had left him an hour ago. He was asleep, and Mu San studied his father's face, fixing it in his memory. He loved his father with a strange intensity. He could not bear to think that he might never see him again. He was his father's favorite, despite the fact that he was the concubine's son. Nothing had been denied him. When his father had seen his disappointment over being called away from his studies in Peking to join the family in their flight from the Reds who were advancing on Shanghai, he had given him funds to travel in England and America and at a time when money was needed to establish the family in Hong Kong. The hazardous and important journey now to be undertaken was in his father's eyes, Mu San knew, the seal placed on his maturity.

Gently Mu San touched his father's hand lying inert on his knee. At the unusual touch, Mr. Chen was instantly awake and alert. For a little he studied the young man standing before him—the handsomest of all his sons, the most clever. He was ready to assume family responsibility —the long tutelage was over. At last he spoke: "You have conducted yourself well in the negotiations this evening. I have placed upon you an infinitely difficult task. Act wisely, move with caution."

The father paused, what further he had to say was painful to him. "I have not made the decision to send you on this journey lightly, my son. Ever since you left Peking you have been restless and unhappy. For what reason I do not know, but I have been fearful. Since this terrible curse of communism fell on China, filial piety has been set at naught, and no man any longer is sure of the loyalty of his sons. Since your return from your trip abroad I have had you watched. I did not take you into my confidence until I felt certain of your loyalty. As you know, until recently I have led you to believe that I am merely operating a fleet of junks—for the purpose of smuggling tools out of Hong Kong into China. The smuggling of a commodity the Reds want hides my real business. I am now giving you your first assignment in the second business. Tonight I am conferring upon you the high honor of rescuing a member of the family and fulfilling the obligation of your grandfather to a friend."

"You honor me," Mu San replied. His youthful training in calm demeanor stood him in good stead. His face, his body, he held in repose, but it seemed to him his heart would burst through the ribs which caged it in, so great was the tumult of his emotions. It was after Chiang Kaishek's police had raided the dormitory of Peking University . . . that awful night . . . no, he wouldn't think of that terrible experience . . . that he had come to believe China's salvation lay in communism—but was it necessary, as the Communists claimed, to desert father and mother in order to serve the State?

While he was abroad he had been relieved of decision, but now his father had placed in his hands the opportunity not only to return to China but to stay and help in China's reconstruction. But to do so would mean deserting the foreigner and failing to rescue Third Uncle, thus betraying his father's trust. The filial piety of a superior man made such an act a hideous thing; but then the new teaching made it right: you belong to the State, you do not belong to your father. What he was thinking of doing was a lofty act of patriotism and it blotted out all other loyalties. The American took on gigantic proportions, became the embodiment of all foreign aggressors. It lay in Mu San's power to make a dupe of this man come to beg a favor, trading on the concept of the superior man. He would deliver him to be dealt with as a spy—lose his life in symbolic retribution for a hundred years of such acts as foisting opium on the Chinese at the point of a gun. Like a high peak from which the ice never melts, sending its coldness down into the warm valley below, the cold decision to deliver this foreigner for punishment chilled even Mu San's love for his father. "How do I get in touch with the right people after we leave the junk?" he asked, his voice calm and measured.

"I am only one link," said his father. "The laodah will turn you and the American over to someone on shore known to him."

"And then—?"

"I cannot tell you. No man knows more than his own part. But you will in time reach Shanghai. There you will be given instructions as to how to get in touch with Third Uncle. Go now to the mother of the family, then to *your* mother, but be careful what you say to her. Return here when you are ready for the journey."

Mu San ascended the stairs and knocked on the door of the head wife's apartment. He found her half-hidden behind the silk curtains of her bed. She wished none of the modern trappings—soft foreign beds softened the spirit as well as the body. He bowed before her, saying, "With your permission I will now depart on business for the family."

When he visited his own mother, she bounced up from her chair as he entered. "Don't think I don't know what is going on in this house," she said. "Third Uncles are precious but sons cannot be spared. And sons must have sons. Your marriage, little one—"

"Marriage, marriage, you talk of nothing else!" Mu San spoke with some petulance. Except in this one matter his mother was indulgence itself toward him.

"There's no use mourning for this Fu Fu you talk about. She's a Communist by now," she answered, disregarding his irritation with her.

"I don't believe it," he replied hotly, then wondered why. Was he not contemplating becoming one? Once he reached China he would be free of the family, free to marry whom he chose. — — — What was he thinking! Free of the family! Stripped of the family! No! In this instant he was the man his father believed him to be. He stood proudly before his mother. "I must leave you for a time. When I return I will accept marriage but I must choose the woman. Now I must return to my father, who has honored me tonight with a place in family affairs."

"Go, then," she said.

Hearing his son's step on the stairs, Mr. Chen rose and

went to the door. Together, without a word's being spoken between them, father and son walked to a room hidden deep in the house—a small room possibly designed by its original owner for storage space. Lying as it did in the very heart of the house, it had been chosen by the late head of the family as a fitting place for the ancestral tablets. The walls had been painted white; the tablets put in their places by his own hands. Against the high window the branches of a tree continually brushed. Beneath the window stood the altar table, on it incense burned in a three-legged bronze bowl.

A froth of white flowers indicated that mourning for Mu San's grandfather who so recently had arranged the tablets—his own now among them—was not over. Father and son knelt before their ancestors, the deep and secret ever-flowing river of the family, the subterranean stream of the dead feeding the bright flashing stream of the living. There with his father Mu San knelt in reverent respect, establishing harmonious communion between the living and the dead, binding himself into the perpetual duties of the family.

As he rose, the individualist in Mu San, born out of Western learning, rebelled at such a subordination of self. But if he remained in the family he must live in Hong Kong and he would be a man without a country, dependent for safety upon the Western exploiters of this island. He would be useless, doing nothing to bring his country back to greatness—an idler, enjoying the family's riches as his brothers did. But if he joined the New China, committing himself to the lofty ideals of the State, he could never again enter the stream of the family. He felt cold hatred of the West which had stolen his mind away from the wisdom of his people. His shoulders shook with the terrible dilemma confronting him.

David was grateful for Mu San's understanding of the need to prepare the mind for such a journey as they were undertaking, but weariness overcame him. He had an hour, he would lie down and rest for a little. Had he slept? Had he dreamed? All at once he seemed to have been lifted out of himself—his destiny was clear to him—his life given to China as his father's had been. Damon could not substitute for him.

Quickly he stood up, went about his preparations. As in childhood, he now floated his lonely, separate self upon China's surging life. He listened for the downbeat of quiet followed by the tumultuous upbeat. It was always thus among the Chinese—all the members of a family never seemed to sleep at the same time, throughout the night living went on.

He heard a woman calling for food. A woman servant stumped along a corridor. Laughter, fast-spoken guttural Chinese words, voices rising and falling in tones high, low, the rush of children's feet in soft-soled shoes, giggling, the scrape of a Chinese violin, a spatter of English spoken by young voices coming up from the hall. A door was shut. He rose and looked out the window. Two couples were leaving for some late party, he supposed. He saw them cross the strip of lawn to the cars. Such gusto for living! Such a society could not crumble! He need not fear that communism, a Western doctrine, could destroy a people cemented together by thousands of years of family life. He would find China essentially what it had always been.

A knock at the door. Mu San entered.

Mu San drove them down to the waterfront, through back streets of poverty which scarred this singularly beautiful island. High old houses, heaped one upon the other, reeked of dirt and poverty. From them came wails of infants, groans of the sick, guttural noises of men pushing food into their bellies with the ravenous haste of animals, reek of rancid oil being thrown into hot and unclean kettles, stench of decayed garbage, acrid odor of night soil. It was a hot night. Almost underfoot here and there lay men asleep—a moment, an hour stolen from the fight against hunger, misery, sickness. The sleep of China's poor was only a throttled moment in the endless struggle to keep alive. There was not room for pity or cleanliness, let alone beauty, among China's millions. Unborn generations hurried upon the heels of the living.

The Western side of David awoke. He had nothing in common with a people so careless and wasteful of the individual. What romantic nonsense had he been indulging in, listening to the outworn empty talk of the superior man who cultivated himself but disregarded the plight of his inferiors? He, David Conway, was an American; certainly he didn't have to live up to the Chinese code. He would tell young Chen that he wasn't going through with the undertaking, demand to be taken to the hotel. Back in his own country, he would soon forget the whole affair. But he could not rid himself of his own heritage. What would his father think of his son's betrayal of Paul Damon, for betrayal David now regarded it. In China lay redemption.

They were climbing now. Soon they were through the pass and on the road leading down to the back of the island. They reached Aberdeen, where tall mast after tall mast, shadowy forms in the night, stood against the sky. Out beyond on the still waters of the harbor the acetylene lamps on the fishing boats brought to David's mind the festival of the dead, when paper lanterns set upon the great Yangtse lighted the way for the spirits of boatmen drowned during the year—always memories.

A few miles farther on and Mu San stopped the car. "The inlet we want has no road to it. We must walk the rest of the way. It's not far."

As he followed Mu San down a steep slope from the road above, David heard the sound of shifting gears. Someone was driving away the car they had come in. Then silence. It was very, very still. They waited a little, then moved forward to the shore. The night was nearly over and the young moon had sunk. A hand grasping his guided David along a plank to a seat in a sampan.

Soon they were alongside a great junk. Strong hands reached down to help them aboard. Standing silent side by side, they listened to the great oar moving backward and forward as the seagoing junk was maneuvered out of the inlet, then the creaking of the central sail being pulled up the central mast.

Using the polite phrases to which he had been reared, but with a wry twist of his mouth which David could not see, Mu San asked, "Would the honorable Conway join my inferior self in our humble quarters?"

"After a little," David answered, wanting to be alone. For a time he sensed the mass of the mountain of Hong Kong looming over them, merely a thick mass of darkness in the dark night. Gradually he became conscious of the coming of daylight upon the water more than in the sky. Mist and distance hid the mountain, the last stronghold of his own people.

Chapter 4

FOR A LITTLE LONGER DAVID surveyed the sky, the sea, then walked slowly aft toward the cabins. Shaped to fit the stern, they rose from the deck in tiers like the caves of Indian cliff dwellers. The third tier was set back from the second, the second from the first, leaving narrow platforms, runways by which the cabins on the upper tiers could be reached. The low doors to these nesting places of the boatmen and their families were closed, for it was very early. The top tier had two cabins. In the area between a man stood, his hands on a long tiller. Occasionally he moved forward, backward. Seeing David, he called out, "Just below they await you."

David caught immediately the arrangement. The steersmen, possibly the younger sons of the owner, were huddled in the small cabins at the sides of the tiller. Probably the captain's family occupied the largest cabin opening on the deck. He and Mu San were to occupy the middle tier. He took the three crude steps which led to its narrow platform. Two doors confronted him; the one to the right was open. He motioned toward it. The steersman nodded.

Stooping, David entered and found Mu San lying on a pallet, one of two on the floor of the cabin. In the small space in front the servant who was to serve them while they were on the junk was squatted fanning a charcoal fire in a small brazier. Two bamboo stools flanked the stove. If the rude planks which made the door and which were now slid back were closed, the place would be without light. Just above his head David heard the soft pat of the steersman's bare feet as he stepped forward and backward, and the accompanying creak of the rudder post. Through the thin wooden partition dividing the cabin in two came the sounds of men, women and children just wakening.

"Chow ready," said the servant. Mu San rose, motioned David to one of the stools, took the other himself. When the servant handed each a steaming bowl of rice-gruel, he ate ravenously, paying no attention to his companion, ignoring the amenities of his people toward a guest sharing a meal. Now and then David glanced at the young Chinese, trying to figure out what was the cause of his sudden shift to impoliteness. Throughout the preparations for this journey he had displayed both graciousness and cooperation. Now he was again rude as he had been during the previous day.

61

Had he, David, in any way offended this sensitive, temperamental young man? If so, when and how?

After they had finished their meal, hoping to restore a more friendly relationship, so necessary to their joint undertaking, David suggested that they take advantage of the good day and make use of the deck. When he received no response to his suggestion, he rose and went out. All around him was a hubbub of activity as the boat people went about the day's business: cooking their morning meal on open braziers placed on the narrow platforms, nursing their babies, tethering others by wide cloth bands to iron rings in the cabin's sides, mending sail.

David lay down on the deck where he was sheltered from the direct rays of the sun by the huge central sail. It hung above him like wings folded back upon each other. Light played across the highly varnished brown deck boards and upon the brown bodies of the boatmen as they passed him to tend the central sail and the smaller ones fore and aft. Sunshine and shadow, the sound of water falling away from the prow, the multitudinous rise and fall of voices— women calling to the men, to the children, giving orders, scolding, laughing—the overflowing life of China which had lulled David to sleep as a child, put a spell on him now which eased him of the tension he had felt ever since he had learned of Paul Damon's fate. Now he would sleep, not the sleep induced by drugs wherein he had so often of late abdicated the domain of self in search of oblivion but natural sleep. Little by little he pressed on into the mystery of sleep—heavy eyelids, heaviness of limb . . . a final letting go. But he did not lie helpless as he had under drugs; somewhere below consciousness he wandered on the timeless beaches of memory seeking renewal.

When, hours later, the wind rose and fluttered his shirt, tapping it gently against his skin, he woke, not knowing for the moment where he was, so real to him was the world which he had inhabited in sleep. Then, as the events which had placed him on this junk came back to him, this other world began slipping from him.

Hastily he reached for those who had occupied it with him, figures out of his childhood—John Conway, his father, six-feet-three in his stocking feet and weighing two hundred pounds, his thighs thick, his shoulders almost too broad for David when he was little to straddle, his hands large but not thick, clever, effective hands. His laugh came out of the deep cavern within him, though his voice was soft; his eyes, a clear, lakelike blue, under emotion became blue-black as water does under heavy clouds.

His mother, her brown hair in a thick braid crowning the top of her head, seemed to make it almost too heavy to be supported by her slender neck. Frail and beautiful, forever drawn to the magnet of her husband's substantial self. But her face . . . he could not conjure up out of that far-off past when she had been a part of his and his father's life.

Amah stood out in detail, a short, firmly built peasant woman, round face, thick lips, shrewd black eyes, clad in blue trousers and jacket, a white butcher's apron covering her ample front, held up by a loop hooked over an intertwined bit of braid which did duty as a button at the neck of her jacket. Like a ship under sail, she stumped along on her bound feet, her strong, vigorous voice often raised in admonition to him, to the servants, to his mother, even to his father. He could see her holding out her arms to him—and her voice—"Shao Con," she always called him.

For a little the three hovered over him as they had in his childhood. Then they left him, and he was conscious only that he was cramped from long hours of sleep and sore from the hard boards of the junk bearing him to a future obscure and uncertain. He rose and looked out over the sea to the coastline of China far off to the left. There lay his destiny, he brooded, unless he met it here on the China Sea, which since far back in time had been plagued by pirates and lashed to frenzy by typhoons.

Day after day, for long hours at a time, the junk moved swiftly under full sail if there was a wind; propelled by the auxiliary engine if there was none. When other junks appeared, they idled and threw out fishing nets to give the appearance of innocence in case the approaching craft be a Communist patrol seeking out illegitimate cargo junks. When they entered the straits between the mainland and Formosa, the laodah ordered both sail and auxiliary engine used. Speed was necessary lest a heavily armed raider from Formosa bent on blockading Red China suddenly put out from the shore and seize them.

Once out of the straits the days became a monotonous repetition of sun, calm sea, no threat of capture, no threat of storm. More and more aware of the dangerous mission upon which he had embarked, troubled by Mu San's continuous hostility, tormented by his responsibility for Paul Damon's plight, David sought in his memory for someone in his life who would bring him the strength he needed. There was his wife—of her he must not think. His father in their long years of companionship—hastily he backed away from such memories because of his father's tragic death. His parents, young, happy, had appeared in his dream that first day on the junk stilling the conflict within him. Might they not now?

Often during his life David had thought of himself as the warring product of the diversified natures of his parents. But now he would view them separate from himself; he would try to evaluate the events over which he had no control but which had determined that he be a man of two countries—his heritage in one, his birth in another. He believed he could now survey dispassionately the shaping of both himself and his parents to China's destiny—something he had never allowed himself to do before, and in so doing he would unify his life.

He would make no effort to distinguish between his memory and what he had learned later from his father's fragmentary writings and his mother's diary found among his father's papers after his death. Neither would he try to distinguish between the fantasies of his childhood and the judgment he had passed on his parents in later years. Out of all these strands their lives and his were woven together in an intricate fabric and so it should remain.

He would begin with the Boxer rebellion. Odd, that an event so remote from the inland American town where his parents had lived should have been the long hand of chance which had reached out and touched them on the shoulder, claiming them for China. The Boxer uprising had brought to a focus the long-held opinion of forward-looking Chinese officials that if they were not to experience continuous defeat at the hands of the West they must learn the techniques which made it strong, which had made even the Far Eastern country of Japan, their inferior for centuries, able to win over them in war. After the Boxer uprising, when the West had exacted heavy penalties from China for her attempt to drive Western representatives out of the country, Chinese officials had gone to America to invite engineers to return with them to teach their sons modern techniques. It was pure coincidence that they had chosen John Conway from a list of men recommended to them by the professors of his university.

What David had failed to understand before was why his father, a civil engineer interested in the development of his own country and in raising an American family, should have so easily given up the opportunities open to him at home to accept a position to teach the youths of another country. In his present objective mood he saw that his father had looked upon China as a primitive country which should be made to take its place in the modern technical world. To do so, China needed trained men like himself to help for a few years and that was not too much for him to give.

It was his mother who still puzzled David. She, who had not only acquiesced but welcomed the opportunity to live in a foreign country, seeing in the undertaking romance and adventure, had sought as far back as David could remember to take away *his* birthright in China which she herself had given to him—something he had resented. Now humbly he set about understanding the total woman, doing it with sympathy, accepting the young, adventurous wife, attempting to reconcile her with that other woman, his mother, who had held *him* back from adventure. Did the contradiction lie deep in the nature of woman, something difficult for a man to understand? His father hadn't understood, nor had he in the past. Could he now?

He tried to envision the young wife carried away by love of the beauty she found in China. He had only what he could remember from her diary to help him. Her written words, as they came to him now, were transcended with the wonderment and delight which she had experienced when she stood on the station platform in Peking with her husband, John, waiting for the Chinese gentleman who had promised to meet them, and had looked up and seen for the first time the towering structure topped by three balconies, each with its green-tiled roof, the corners curved skyward in rhythmic lines.

In a few moments three Chinese gentlemen had made their dignified way through the crowd on the platform and stopped before them. Bowing low, each shook his own hands in greeting. Then these silk-clad men, so exquisite, so elegant in her eyes, had escorted them to a Western hotel in the center of the Legation Quarter just inside the city wall and overshadowed by it. Time after time, during the night, she had awakened in strange excitement, a mingling of wonder and awe. Out there in the night was the city wall—that medieval structure—mysterious and beautiful.

The next morning, before the appointed hour for the Chinese gentlemen to escort them to their new home, she had wandered with John about the legation center. Through open gates she glimpsed beautiful gardens, impressive Western houses. One of them might be the very house which was to be her home.

Mingling with these memories of his mother were memories of his father. If the legation center was indicative of the way they were to live, he had relinquished the vigorous outdoor activities of a civil engineer benefitting his own country, for ease and comfort. There was no evidence of a frontier here. And he had tied himself up for three years! But as they passed along by the wall surrounding the British Legation he noticed the inscription, "Lest We Forget" over a bit of it which was bullet scarred. So this was the barricade behind which Western men, women, and children had taken refuge against the attacks of the Boxers! John, who had had the siege described to him by a man on the steamer, had pictured the wall as high and all but impregnable. But this wall, only a few inches higher than his own head, the Chinese could have climbed easily and, in a couple of hours, wiped out all the Westerners. It was undoubtedly the greater intelligence of the Westerners within which had held the fanatical Boxers at bay until the foreign troops arrived a month later and rescued them. Civilized people don't do things like this, thought John Conway, and his faith in his own value to this country came back to him. He was needed here; but he was thankful his young wife had not seen this historic inscription or the bullet-scarred wall; it might have frightened her.

Soon after their return to the hotel, the Chinese gentlemen had arrived to escort them to their new home. John, viewing them in the light of his reactions to that bit of wall, felt a trifle on the defensive, especially when they spoke of the mean dwelling they had secured and which they, unworthy as they were, were placing at the disposal of the honored teacher. Honored nothing, thought John, if they can't do better than that. Emily, conscious of the beautiful houses she had just seen, had her first feeling of disappointment.

After a ride in rickshas through dusty streets filled with men pulling loads too heavy even for animals—a sight which disturbed his mother, and made his father indignant —the rickshas came to an abrupt stop before a black-lacquered gate with an elaborate brass knocker. Immediately the two halves of the gate swung open. The Chinese gentlemen led them past a gatehouse, down a passageway, and suddenly harmony and beauty lay before them, disarming them both. A well-proportioned court was bounded by low gray dwellings with beautifully curved roofs. Red-lacquer pillars supported the shallow verandas, windows intricately latticed with dark wood broke the gray expanse of house walls. When they stepped inside, the paper panes glowed like mother-of-pearl. The place spoke of magnificence unmatched by the America they knew. (Later they learned that this court was one of many courts of a small palace once owned by a prince.) Five servants stood at attention! Emily, charmed with such a setting, believed with so many servants to help her she could overcome the difficulties of stone floors and the lack of modern sanitation. John, although he deplored such inefficiency, accepted the arrangement with good grace thinking that living as the Chinese lived would bring him in closer touch with his students.

During the weeks that followed, his parents, who had come to teach the superiority of the West, found that instead the Chinese appeared to be instructing them. Quietly but persistently the dutiful and polite servants shaped his mother into their ancient mold. Lightheartedly, she accepted the servants' dictum—face for one was face for all, master, mistress and servants a unit of solidarity, dignity and grace—and left the care of the house to them as all along, she discovered later, they had intended her to do. It was in that house that he, David, had been born.

So also did his students shape David's father, but not easily. On the first day when, aware of the importance of his mission, John Conway strode into the classroom designated as his, he found himself facing a group of young men who would have made any self-respecting civil engineer in America resign in disgust. They were as elegant as women in dress and build. John soon learned that, sons of officials, they belonged to the scholar class, which was above manual labor. They were dressed as custom decreed such gentlemen should be. Their long queues, supplemented with silken cord, hung in straight lines down the backs of their silk gowns, which reached to their ankles. Many of them had grown inch-long nails on their little fingers, indicating superiority to labor.

John longed to send these elegant youths out with surveying instruments into Peking's dusty streets and dirty them up a bit, teach them the value of labor. But before they could tackle an engineer's job, he would have to teach them something of mathematics and drafting. Intending to have no nonsense, he began his teaching by emphasizing promptness and industry; but immediately he found his pupils had no idea of coming to class on time—or coming at all if family duties or pleasures interfered—and they brought their servants to carry their books and set up their drafting boards! But trained to handle a writing brush, an occupation fitting to a gentleman, they worked with precision and accuracy on mechanical drawings.

John introduced what he considered the rudiments of efficiency, forbidding servants to attend their masters in the classroom. When a particularly elegant youth refused to give up his servant, John expelled him from the class. Then all Chinese officialdom descended on his hapless head. The cobweblike structure—official family intertwined with official family—trembled to the utmost, outer strands. Loss of face to one was loss of face to all. To John's consternation the university ceased to function. Nothing could proceed until face was restored to the young man. Of necessity John reinstated the boy and all went on as before.

At home he found it was much the same. "It is the custom," the houseboy or cook would say, and the whole complicated business of running the household of a scholar, teaching the sons of officials, was brought to a stop until custom was re-established. "After all, you can't combat a two-thousand-year precedent," Emily would lightheartedly admonish her husband.

Chapter 5

SOMETIME DURING THESE first weeks of their residence in China his parents had done what all foreigners who came to this imperial city did—climbed to the top of the wall of the Tartar City to look down on the four cities placed one within another, like a set of boxes. Carefully they picked their way up the ramp among weeds, rough grass, and broken brick. "Not much initiative displayed here," said John. But when they reached the top and looked down they were silent for a long time, held spellbound by the grandeur of the scene spread out below.

At the center of rows upon rows of gray-tiled roofs, set

off into great blocks by broad streets running from east to west, from north to south, was an immense enclosure of gleaming, shining yellow roofs. As their eyes grew accustomed to the brilliance, they saw that the Forbidden City, for such it was, was a balanced pattern of noble spaces surrounded by shallow buildings roofed with yellow tiles, acre upon acre, the yellow curved roofs sparkling in the brilliant northern sunlight. A green filigree of delicate willows lent grace to this stylized home of emperors.

From a yellow-roofed gate in the red wall which surrounded this city, a wide thoroughfare led through a gate in the Imperial City to the towering gate of the Tartar City, the battlements on which they now stood. They walked around the bastion, sheltered from the sun by its green-tiled roofs. From the south side they looked out over the parapet into a fourth city. Far away in the distance they could see a grove of trees, dark even in the sunlight. This must be the cypress grove in the midst of which they had been told stood the Temple of Heaven and the gleaming marble altar where the Son of Heaven once a year rendered his account to Heaven.

David's father was amazed at the imagination of a nation which had planned the noble spacing, the balanced pattern of the four cities; his mother felt herself transfigured by the beauty which surrounded her. From then on, like so many foreigners before and after her, she became a devotee of this country—a curious surrender of self to a people who had created this wondrous city. Sensitized only to beauty, she found it everywhere—in the embroidered curtains of officials' chairs as they rode through the streets on business or pleasure, their retainers costumed to fit their lords' ranks running ahead to clear the way; she found it in the old bronzes in the temples, in ancient Chinese paintings; she found it in her home, in the quality of diffused light which came through the glazed paper-paned windows, in the perfect proportions of her courtyard, in the exquisite politeness of her servants.

Late into the fall, chrysanthemums filled the courtyard, placed there by the gardener. Whistles fastened to the tails of pigeons circling and swooping above her courtyard filled the air with delicate music. "You like?" the houseboy asked. "My pigeons I bring from my home."

As a climax to all this enchantment was her visit to the Altar of Heaven, a special privilege arranged by the head of the university where John taught. For days after she had seen it she had lived in a kind of ecstasy. The very trees, it seemed to her, had stood back reverently from the vast white marble altar, roofed only by the blue heaven.

Vividly David envisioned the city where he had been born. Beautiful, noble, magnificent, with its golden center and its pure white altar among the cypress trees. In his attempt to re-create the impression it had made upon his mother, he had re-created the impression it so long ago had made upon him. Then suddenly it came to him that the city might have been destroyed by the Communists, who were out to rid China of her past. He must know what had happened. Compulsion drove him forward, hurried him up the steps leading to the second platform of the junk. Making his way between children, hens, women, and cooking stoves, he burst in upon Mu San, who was as usual still

74

lying stretched out on the pallet. "What happened when the Communists took over Peking?" he demanded. "You were there, weren't you? What did they do to the city?"

"Do! What would a scholar like Mao Tse-tung do but repair the damages!"

"Was it damaged by the Japanese?"

"No."

"Then who were the vandals? How much did they destroy?"

"Any city is demoralized before an advancing army," said Mu San, avoiding a direct answer. He must not betray himself by seeming to uphold the Communists; neither did he wish to tell of the degradation of many of the students in the months before communism took over. It was humiliating to admit that students under any provocation could sink below the traditional high standard set by Confucius for scholars.

Noticing the look of distress on his companion's face, David did not press him for more information. Instead he said, "I, too, am grateful to the Reds if, as you say, they have preserved Peking. You know I was born there."

"The new government has restored Peking's imperial grandeur," said Mu San with dignity. Suddenly the terrible decision whether to choose his family or his country seemed to have been made. To turn away from communism was to turn back to the degradation of the last year of Chiang Kai-shek's regime when Peking had sunk deep into its own despair—dirt, filth, crumbling buildings, bad government, intimidation. Refugee students who had fled before the advancing Communists had camped in the grounds of the Temple of Heaven. Left without resources promised them by the government, living in squalor and idleness, they sprawled about in the temple, and defiled the altar; their fresh and dried excrement littered it.

But Mu San did not intend that the foreigner should know that China's elite, for so the student had always been considered, could sink so low. "Chiang's troops were quartered in the Temple of Heaven enclosure," he said. "They cut down the ancient cypress trees for firewood." Mu San was glad to tell of the soldiers' vandalism, for it gave him the opportunity to speak against Chiang Kai-shek, whom he hated. "But when Mao Tse-tung's troops came into the city," he added, "they urged students as well as workmen to restore everything that could possibly be restored before Mao Tse-tung's arrival ... the students were proud to help clear away debris from the temple and palace grounds ... with their own hands they did it."

Shocked over the destruction Nationalist troops had wrought but relieved to know that the Reds had restored the city's beauty, David talked about this place and that in Peking, dear to him—lakes, marble bridges in the Forbidden City, the blue-roofed, circular Temple of Heaven, and the altar, which his mother had never ceased to love. "Have they repaired the altar?" he asked. "For years it was neglected."

"Yes," replied Mu San.

"And the Forbidden City?"

"At great expense."

"I would have thought they would have no use for an emperor's dwelling."

76

"I don't want you to misunderstand me, Conway. When I said the Communists had restored it and at much expense, I did not mean they believe in such trappings. They preserve them as a symbol of our past glory when the whole world paid tribute to China. Mao Tse-tung believes the world will again pay homage."

"And do you believe it?" David asked, startled by the idea.

"I do not know." Had he said too much, given himself away? Mu San got to his feet and went out on the platform in front of the cabin and faced into the wind to cool his cheeks flushed with emotion. For him, too, by his conversation with David, that imperial city had been re-created. He saw it as it had been on that brilliant day in 1949. In the great square in front of the Forbidden City, an eager throng was gathered. All eyes were on a white pole set in the center of the square; from its top floated a huge blood-red flag, five white stars upon it. A short, stocky figure stood on the bastion of the gatehouse above the great brass-studded gate through which once the tribute bearers of the Western nations had entered to make obeisance before the Yellow Dragon Throne. Now a savior had been raised up to bring China back her lost glory. Again nations would tremble at the power of China! Guns roared. The triumph of the revolution, *The New Government!* From thousands of throats rose the cry, "Mao Tse-tung! Mao Tse-tung!"

Before Mao Tse-tung rumbled tanks, armored lorries, machine guns, the paraphernalia of modern war—American equipment captured from Chiang Kai-shek's troops, evidence to him of America's shameful participation in

China's civil war. The hard core of Communist troops came next, the soldiers who had made the long march with Mao Tse-tung; then students; then the gayly clad bands of women, the Yang-ko, dancing the traditional dance of the spring festival—two steps forward, one back—singing, chanting the songs of the New China.

In his childhood Mu San had participated in the spring festival, watched the dancers, heard the drums beat, the cymbals clang. By the delicate perception his elders had passed on to him, he too had partaken of the awakening fertility of the earth—earth's renewal which was stored in the memory of his people, reaching back to the beginnings of time when each spring the maidens lay with the youths upon the fertile earth. And now, joined to the fertility of field and man, the new fertility—mechanized, industrialized productivity, a virile, strong China bursting its old-fashioned sterile mold. Two steps forward, one back, the Yang-ko dancers advanced, singing of the newly created China.

By Mu San's side in the crowd was Lo, his friend and revered teacher, the exquisite scholar with the pointed chin, the lively eyes, the inquiring mind. He it was who had taught Mu San the doctrines of Marx and Mao. Enlightenment and prestige were to come to Peking and the dignity of labor to all China—Mao's doctrine. Lo knelt and bowed to the ground before Mao Tse-tung; Mu San also knelt. The days of degradation and discouragement were gone.

A giant, complex organization created by Mao had moved south, ahead of the troops, to make preparation for rest and food for the soldiers. With them went Yang-ko dancers to perform dramas, to dance and sing, thus to inspire the people—a great advancing horde, disciplined in work, a miracle of organization that moved on, on. They crossed the Yangtse, took Shanghai. Moving south, spreading over all China, they drove Chiang Kai-shek out of the country. Mu San wished he could boast of it all to this wretched foreigner. Foreigners had so often spoken in pity of the Chinese lack of organizing ability; but if he boasted, his father's friend might suspect the son whom he now trusted. Friend, father, son—highly charged words. Mu San's exhilaration ebbed away. The essence of the family— could he deny it?

His mother . . . did he mean to destroy his mother? He remembered the day he had come back from Peking to Shanghai by order of his father, after Mao Tse-tung had entered Peking. He had voiced the new doctrine—the family cleansed, concubines given over to serve the State. His father had sternly reprimanded him. Did he wish to see his mother thrown out of the family? "The strict interpretation of Confucius' teachings is that a man should have but one wife," said his father, "but such strictness gave way before the desire for sons in our family. You know that your grandfather lost his only son, and that I took his place. My wife bore only one son, as you also know. It was your grandfather's wish that I take a concubine. She has borne many children, made the family secure. Now would you have me deny her the protection of the family? Would you, her son? Reforms must come gradually, my son and hers." It was that night that the family had fled from

79

Shanghai and of his own accord Mu San had accompanied it. If he joined the New China, he opened the way to the destruction of the family. Betrayal of the family? Then he no longer would have any right to its name. He belonged to the name, not the name to him.

David, looking out through the doorway of the cabin, thoughtfully studied the young Chinese. His black hair, cut long enough to hang about his ears in the manner of Mao Tse-tung's, a splendid disguise for a man in the underground, was flung straight back by the wind. His shoulders, too, were flung backward. Whatever the young man's conflict—and conflict there evidently had been—it seemed to have ended in victory. Or had it? Suddenly the young man's shoulders sagged. He turned; in turning he faced David, who stared unbelievingly at Mu San's contorted features, his twisted mouth, burning eyes, the knotted muscles of his cheeks. Never before had David seen such an expression in a Chinese face! All the changes wrought in Chinese thought by the West had never succeeded in destroying completely the basic immobility of the Chinese expression; some deep quietude of the spirit had always remained untouched by the restless searching spirit of Western thought. But now it seemed that this young man's inner, heretofore inviolate, center had been rent asunder.

David felt himself reaching out for his father's guidance. John Conway would have understood the young Chinese so suddenly thrust into the agonizing situation of entering his own country as a fugitive. Yes, that was it; for the first time David grasped the terrible strain the young Chinese must be under—admiring the New China, as he evidently did, he served the old. That was why Mu San had so continuously stayed in the cabin. He wished to be alone to solve this conflict.

David rose, thinking to give Mu San the privacy he needed. At that moment young Chen stepped blindly into the cabin and the two confronted each other. The hate which leaped up in young Chen's eyes made the older man draw back.

Deeply disturbed, David went back to the deck. The sun was disappearing into the calm waters. Twilight was beginning to clothe the sea. Peace lay all around, but he could not capture it for himself. Was Mu San possibly mixed up with the Reds? But he couldn't be! If he was, he would not take this dangerous way of entering China. David tried to shake off his growing sense of distrust in his companion, but he could not forget the hatred in the eyes of the young Chinese and he could no longer shirk the fact that it was directed at him. Was it not madness for him to trust a Chinese so obviously hating the West, hating him? Surely it was suicidal to go on with this impossible journey. Even if Mu San was not mixed up with the Reds he would be, in his present mood, a doubtful ally. At the best his hatred for David and his necessity to regard him as a friend in order to meet the Chinese concept of right conduct were emotions in unstable equilibrium. Some small act on David's part might anger Mu San and drive him into deserting the man who stood for all he hated in the West. There was still an opportunity for David to save himself. He had only to declare the journey off, stay on the junk for its return trip to Hong Kong. No one would blame him if he refused to enter a country given over to cruelties such as they had inflicted upon Paul Damon—Damon! He had betrayed Paul Damon! He must think, he must find some place on the junk where *he* could be alone.

Seeing the sail on the foremast was down and the bow was empty, he went forward, eagerly grasping at the privacy thus mercifully afforded him. In the gathering darkness he looked down at the waters falling away before the junk. On the sides of the prow he saw stains where the blood of many fowls had drained down—the sacrifice offered before each journey for a safe return.

Throughout the night, with the sound of the waters cleft in two by the moving junk, he sought to resolve his own conflict, tried to decide between what his mother and father would counsel him in this hour, but surely he did not have to decide between them, simply make his peace with them both and they with him. Surely he could now have their united approval to give up this perilous undertaking. If he could resolve their conflict, he could resolve his own.

And yet was it not he who had driven them apart, for the change in his mother had come about in those first months in which she had carried him in the safety of her womb. He should not resent the change in her. It was the desire to guard him after his birth, as before, which had wrought the change in her.

The months before his birth she had been the paramount consideration of the whole household. Birth was the supreme concern of a people whose immortality lay in the continuance of the family. The stream that was the family must never be interrupted. His mother was precious now as the vehicle of immortality. Served, waited upon, cared for. Specially prepared dishes of fish, beautifully rounded fruits and cakes, carefully chosen symbols of fertility, were brought to her to eat. The amah, hired by the houseboy, ate of them too, for amah also was pregnant—selected because the months of her pregnancy coincided with those of the mistress. Therefore she would be able to nurse the master's child and thus support two sons already born to her, as well as the child to come—if a boy. Amah, along with all the others, connived to protect the mistress. Furthermore, she made offerings at a nearby temple to the goddess of mercy asking that they both bear sons.

Living in the world of beauty she had found in China, sheltered, ministered to by everyone around her, including her husband, who felt an added tenderness toward her just now, Emily did not suspect that John was deeply troubled. How could she? The powerful forces which were shaping his father were forces opposite to those shaping his mother.

His father was not sheltered by this old civilization as she was; rather, he was opposed by those around him whose habits, fixed for centuries, he was destroying. Almost immediately he had perceived that the Chinese were highly endowed mentally; also that they deliberately until now had turned away from scientific knowledge. Did they have a fundamental distrust of its value—for them at least? On the long ricksha rides across the city to the university, always aware of the human effort of the man in the shafts of the ricksha pat-patting along the dusty streets, John

Conway did more thinking than he had ever done in his life before. What was he doing to the minds of the young men he was teaching? He knew nothing of Chinese history or philosophy. Incredible to him that he should have undertaken to teach a people of whom he had no knowledge or understanding. Was he creating good or destroying it?

Believing that, if he were not to do harm, he must know something of the traditions of the students he taught, he sought out Westerners who had lived long in the country, asking how best to go about his study. An Englishman, Sir Francis Humboldt, who possessed a library given over completely to books about China, hearing of the young engineer's eagerness to acquire more than a superficial knowledge of the Chinese, extended to him the privilege, granted to few, of reading his treasured books.

One day, sitting in this quiet library reading a history of the West's effort to penetrate the closed country of China, John came upon a passage written by an emperor in 1839 in which he made it plain that he did not wish to deal with envoys sent out from England. "As your ambassador can see, we possess all things," the passage read. "I see no value in objects strange or ingenious and have no use for your country's manufactures." The young engineer put down the book. Quickly his thoughts moved forward to the Boxer uprising of nineteen-hundred . . . Was China not saying the same thing in the twentieth century as the ancient emperor had said so long ago but saying it in more violent terms? And yet, he, John Conway, was here to introduce technical knowledge and here by invitation! Again he asked himself what it was that China wished to gain from the West? Not, he was convinced, Western thought. Reading and thinking, he came to believe that the Chinese wanted Western tools simply as a means to preserve their own way of life, and that they did not understand the disturbing nature of the industrial revolution. If accepted, what would technical skill do to this overpopulated land?

It must have been some time later, David surmised, that Sir Francis came into his library one day while John Conway was there. Glancing at an empty place on the shelf which held books on Chinese philosophy, and then at the strong, powerfully built engineer, obviously a man of action, who was evidently absorbed in reading the book on Chinese philosophy, Sir Francis' interest was piqued. To delve into the diaphanous world of Oriental thinking was a hard task for any man. "Do you find something in such a book, Mr. Conway, that bears on your work?" he asked, sitting down by the side of the young engineer.

"How my work bears on it, I should say."

"Are you perhaps concerned that our Western ideas, if accepted, might destroy the talismanic jewel hidden in the dross of exquisite idleness? You know, of course, that physical effort is not countenanced by the Chinese scholar?"

"Something like that," John answered, "if I know what you mean."

The Englishman did not explain.

It was after this conversation that his father, David believed, had decided that he must study the language if he was to learn what was this talismanic jewel. He, who until recently had found his greatest interest in the drafting board and the physical work of surveying, undertook to study for several hours each day with a Chinese teacher and to memorize hundreds of characters—the minimum he would need to read even the simplest Chinese writings.

Gradually, through the medium of books, language, and the friendship of Sir Francis, his Chinese teacher, and the impact that daily struggles with his students to get them to accept Western concepts made upon him, John Conway began to penetrate a little into Chinese thought—the Confucian way—a cult of the superior man. The scholars were an elite group governing the shao ren, the little people. The superior man observed meticulously the duty of son to father, of friend to friend. Was this the talismanic jewel? What troubled John Conway was that this cult of personality ignored the plight of the common man.

Winter came with its bitter cold, its periodic dust storms, brown silt from the Gobi Desert carried into Peking on the high southwest winds. On such days few ventured out of their houses into the dust-drenched air. These times of seclusion, accepted as inevitable by all who ever lived in Peking, were welcomed by John Conway. When his school was closed for the long New Year celebration, he shut himself into the seclusion his study offered and attempted to submerge himself in Chinese thought. But the more he studied, the more troubled he became.

One afternoon toward twilight as he sat in his study deeply troubled, finding no solution to his problem, he was conscious of real tranquillity all around him—order and peace. The coolie came in to mend the fire in the stove, the boy entered asking in deferential tones if he would care to have his lamp lighted. He could hear amah and Emily in the next room talking together each in her own language, but somehow communicating with each other. All at once it struck him that his wife seemed to understand these people better than he. He knew enough about them now to realize that this contentment in his house could not exist if Emily wasn't in harmony with them. He rose and went into the living room, where she was showing amah a new knitting stitch.

At his entrance amah rose from her knees beside her mistress and murmuring something about "the master" clumped out of the room on her bound feet.

"John, how nice!" Emily exclaimed. "I was wishing you'd come in. Isn't this lovely—the servants brought it to me." She picked up a wooden figure of a woman holding a child. "It's their madonna. They call her . . ."

"Kwan Yin," he supplied the Chinese word. Then without preparing her, forgetting he had protected her until now from his perplexities, he burst out, "Emily, I'm troubled. I want your help. I'm troubled over what I may be doing—what effect I may be having on the boys I am teaching. I might do a lot of harm. These people don't *think* the way we do, and I can't seem to find out how they think."

"Must you know *how* they think?" she asked, looking up in surprise at his unwonted outburst. "Why can't you just do your job? I believe we should not try to penetrate their minds."

Attempting to bridge the gap which he now realized

87

existed between his thinking and that of his wife, John spoke slowly, stopping often to put his thoughts into concrete terms. "If you rode, as I do, twice a day around the corner of the Forbidden City, seeing the roofs of the turrets curved upward as no man of the West would ever think of curving them . . . walls and turrets topped with those special yellow tiles . . . tiles sometimes dull, almost sullen-looking on a gray day, brilliant when the sun touches them—" He broke off, feeling powerless to express what he felt. Then he went doggedly on. "Even in a dust storm the imperial color of the tiles is never entirely lost. Behind that wall lives a ruler so secluded the common people must shut themselves within their houses so that their eyes can't rest upon his sacred person when he makes his annual visit to the Temple of Heaven to account for his stewardship. Stewardship? What kind of stewardship, when every day round that wall over a rutty road men pull loads too heavy for an elephant? What is there to preserve? Why shouldn't we try to destroy it? And that's what we're doing. But suppose we destroy something precious . . . and keep what isn't precious?"

"John, aren't you troubling yourself over things which are not your responsibility? Can't you just do what you promised to do—teach engineering? What they make of it is their responsibility, isn't it?"

"You think so?" he asked.

"Why, yes. It seems so to me."

"Emily, the core of their philosophy lies in the superior man. It offends my ideas of democracy. Democracy doesn't

88

go in for an elite. Am I wrong? Listen, Emily. There's an old saying here that a painter must have the bamboo in his heart before he can paint it. Maybe you understand this country better than I do. Maybe you have its meaning in your heart. You seem always able to see it in terms of beauty. Beauty—is that the key to what I'm seeking? Does it lie in the beauty of that yellow-topped wall? Is the genius which created the grandeur and the symmetry of the Forbidden City tied up with the superior man? You have some of the qualities the Chinese people have. They're more feminine than masculine. I'm beginning to think they're the feminine part of the world and should be left so. You know, they believe everything in the world is divided into male and female. Is beauty the answer, Emily?"

Indeed, she thought, he is changed. He is no longer a simple man. "Stay outside," she pleaded. "This country will change you."

"That's happened already. And you—you, too, are changed, Emily."

They looked at each other, each conscious of the change in the other. What was the mysterious power of this country? What would it do to them?

The next morning after his father had left the house his mother had called her ricksha. She would take the route her husband took each day, find out if she could what that ride meant to him. Muffled in shawls, a Chinese foot warmer under her feet, a blanket over her knees, for the day was cold, she took the long ride, insisting that the

89

curtains of the ricksha be lowered to the second hook so that she could look out on the city's streets. Today she was not enthralled by beauty, not even by the watchtowers topped with golden tiles rising majestically above her. Instead she was conscious of the drivers of the carts in straw-stuffed moccasins plodding at the sides of the shaft mules, the half-starved, wolflike dogs, scavengers snarling at each other over a rotted cabbage leaf, a turnip top, children crouching from the cold, holding out thin blue hands for alms. Her ricksha man squeezed past a funeral procession. The paper figures, bright blue, red, attendants for the dead, were borne aloft by men in green and gold robes. It was a pageant of color she had formerly enjoyed. Today she noticed the rags of the beggars who had been hired for the procession, flapping below the green coats, embroidered in gold.

On her way home she remembered sights, sounds, heretofore ignored. Many times passing the wall surrounding the British Legation she had seen the words "Lest We Forget." She had considered it foolish to have such a reminder of an event that should be forgotten—now she was not so sure. And she remembered how sometimes the ugly words "foreign devil" had been hurled at her. And she remembered something that seemed most significant of all—Chinese mothers covering the faces of their children when she passed to protect them from the foreigner's evil spirit. Westerners were alien, indeed, to these people. Resentment engendered by poverty might again erupt and endanger the foreigner. These millions of humble people might, if they were made to suffer too much, make the foreigner their scapegoat.

This ancient country would absorb only as much as it wanted of the West. It would shape John to its own uses. Already it had begun to do so. It would even destroy him if necessary. How had she been so blind as not to see what was happening? Danger lay ahead for her, for her child, and it would come through John, her loving husband, unless she could turn him aside from his purpose.

That evening when all the servants had gone to their quarters, even amah who usually hovered around to help in last ministrations, Emily told John of her ride. "I went," she said, "to try and put myself in your place."

"It was good of you, Emily. Did you feel you could?" he asked, eagerly searching her face for his answer.

"John, I think I understand a good deal more than I did last night and I'm afraid for us."

"Afraid!"

"Listen, John, you and I are simple people. So is our country simple. The complexities of this old civilization are beyond us."

"Perhaps as China is now, yes, but that is because they look backward. Democracy would bring in fresh ideas. What it needs is an industrial revolution—a new birth."

"The old cannot conceive, John."

"Nations can."

"Possibly," she answered, "but not without terrible suffering. You, yourself, said last night that you might destroy something valuable. Think what it would mean to put machines into a country with unlimited manpower. . . and an autocratic ruler."

"But, Emily, do you wish men to go on doing work fit only for animals?"

"I'm not sure they'll be any happier with machines. Look at the old people on the streets. In spite of their poverty they are the happiest looking old people I've ever seen. They understand and accept. But if we interfere—"

"Do you want the despotism that emanates from the Forbidden City to go on?" he demanded.

"Are you sure you'll do away with the despotism? It could be worse with machines."

"If the West has meddled, as you seem to think it has," he countered, "then shouldn't I try to undo any harm I may have done . . . will do in the years I have promised to teach here?"

"John, you have used my words against me so that you could stay in this country. You won't see that we could be hurt. You promised to protect me—and our child. Let us go home now," she begged.

"If you don't want our child born in China, you could leave and come back afterwards. I can't break my word."

"That wouldn't change things. It's you, don't you see?"

"See what?"

"See that this country is exerting its power over you. If you are not careful, it will swallow you up . . . swallow us all up."

"Emily, you exaggerate."

"I think not."

In the weeks that followed, she sought to find in his

books authority for her fears in the hope she could then make an appeal to his reason. She thought she had found it in China's history. In past centuries China had received tribute from the rest of the world.

She said to him, "I think China wants to get her original power back. Aren't you furthering that ambition?"

"But democracy," he protested. "Democracy would change all that."

"They will never accept it," she said, turning away.

"I believe they will," he answered. "In talking to you I've clarified my own thinking."

Intuition told her that he had committed himself to China not only for three years but for his lifetime—if it were necessary to bring Western efficiency and government to China.

She began to lose sight of the grace and beauty still around her. As the time for the birth of her child—David's birth—drew nearer, she grew more and more apprehensive. One night sitting alone in her own room, looking back over the months she had struggled to influence her husband and failed, she felt forces beyond her control menacing her. Sounds coming to her over the walls of the compound seemed sinister and terrible—the deep-toned bells of the passing carts, the cries of the street vendors; even the movements of the servants about the house seemed stealthy. Physical revulsion took hold of her, she was sick and had to call amah, whom of late she had banished from nightly attendance upon her. A few hours later, two months before her time, he, David, was born—born to inherit his

93

parents' conflict. He owed something to this land of his birth, even as his father had felt he did. He did not owe it anything; this was his mother's voice warning him against debarking on an unfriendly shore with an unfriendly companion as a guide.

Chapter 6

WHEN DAY BROKE, A MAN came forward and ran up the foresail. "The honorable one should eat," said the sailor, "we are nearing the destination." Feeling the throb of the auxiliary engine and the swift forward movement of the junk, David felt squeezed and twisted within, too stricken to rise and leave the junk's prow. Then physical sensations of comfort and security rose out of depths within him, absent during his night's vigil. The father he had dreamed about that first afternoon on the junk was again real—strong, weighing two hundred pounds, lifting his little son, tossing him in the air, catching him in his strong arms; he looking down from that citadel

95

into his mother's eyes; she smiling, reaching up, clasping his hand in hers, covering it with hers. His father, Da Con, holding them both in his enormous embrace; the three of them so close. Other strong arms—amah's. "Shao Con, the little Con," she called him—amah's child. Physical sensations of safety.

Then memories focused and orderly crowded in. It was his fifth birthday. It was spring. The sun was shining. A wisteria vine grown into a great tree, its branches wound stoutly around a trellis in the courtyard, sent shifting shadows across the intricate pattern of the latticed windows and down onto the white tablecloth. It was breakfasttime.

His father sat at one end of the table, his mother opposite, and he between. It was seldom now that his mother left her room. She was with them this morning because it was his birthday. He repeated after her the verse she had chosen for him to memorize, usually recited in her room. "In the secret place of the Most High." David pictured the Most High living in secrecy in the Forbidden City.

Early in the afternoon he sat in a low chair by his mother's bedside. And now his happiness over the importance of this day was tinged with anxiety. "When you walk with your father, beg him to take us home so that I, in the time left to me, may teach you to be a good American."

"I am a Peking man," David had cried.

"You are my son, and that makes you an American," his mother had said, "and you must never forget it."

"Peking man." Stubbornly he repeated his declaration.

"David! David!" she cried. "It's only you who can

persuade your father to leave China. I have failed. For my sake, my dear, please try."

He kept his head bowed, but watching furtively he saw tears seep out from under the closed lids of his mother's eyes. "I guess you want to go to sleep," he said. "I make you tired." Trying to copy his father's quiet manner, he rose, smoothed the coverlet under which she lay, and kissed her gently on the cheek.

Her eyes flew open. "David, a wise person never allows himself to be wholly surrendered to other people or ideas, not even to beauty. What your father is showing you today is a magnificent and beautiful sight. Take it into your heart, but let your soul remain free."

Outside the door David knocked roughly against amah, who seemed to spring out of nowhere to block his way. "Amah make proper son to walk with great father."

"Aw, Amah, Dad likes me like this." But there was no cajoling her today. Under her watchful eye he put on the best clothes she had laid out on his bed, the ones he wore to the exclusive English school to which his mother sent him—gray shorts, gray woolen stockings stopping just below the knee, white shirt, short coat. As he did so, gradually his fear over being taken to America subsided. Once more he felt safe.

Amah would never let him go. He had been her child ever since he could remember and long before, according to the tales she had told him. As a very small child, sitting on her lap in the kitchen, he had listened to her and the servants discussing the dramatic events of his birth—a puny baby born prematurely, saved by amah, who the same night forced the birth of her own child that she might nurse the master's child.

There had been a brief struggle between his mother and amah in those first hours after his birth. Despite the doctor's warning that so frail an infant could not wait, his mother had insisted that she would not surrender him to amah. Amah, just as determined that *her* children should not starve for want of her earnings as a wet nurse, waited grimly but confidently. When the doctor put David into her arms she nestled him inside her garments, supplying the warmth of which he had been too early deprived. When she gave him her breast, full and running over, he became her child. The girl she had borne was given to another woman to nurse, to whom amah paid a small sum.

Ever since David could remember amah had had a cot in his room. In the night taking him into her bed she cuddled him within her padded garments close to her warm, soft self, as she had ever since his birth. Long after he had been weaned, she suckled him as she would have one of her own. Dimly, five-year-old David could re member this. Even though for some time she had been banished from his room, the cot was still there for her to use when he had one of his frequent colds. And unbe known to his parents, every night after they were asleep she crept back to "precious" him. Always she seemed to be there leaning over him when he was cold or frightened. And now her grim presence assured him that in some way she would keep him in this country with her.

After he was dressed he had returned to his mother's room for her approval. One small, beautiful hand she had placed under his chin and raised his head so that she could look into his eyes. "Now remember, David, what I told you. If you can't get your father to go, I must take you myself."

As he sat in the gatehouse waiting for his father, he tried to decide what to do. His mother, just like a doll, so tiny, so helpless most of the time—a boy should take care of his mother. But his father did not want to leave China—even his mother said so—and a son obeyed his father and carried out his wishes. Amah, the houseboy, the cook, the coolie, and his Chinese teacher all had taught him to reverence his father. But his mother wanted him to leave this house and all his friends and go to a strange country where amah could not go. Fright again, and then there was his father at the gate calling, "Are you ready, Son?"

Standing between his father's knees he had ridden in the family ricksha, the bell clanging, the ricksha boy shouting, "Open the way! Open the way!" to the foot of the wall surrounding the Tartar City. There, near the great Chien Men Gate, they had climbed the ramp together, still grass-grown, still cluttered with broken stones, just as it had been when his father and mother had climbed it for the first time. Through an embrasure of the wall's parapet he looked over into the outer city. "Now turn, Son, and see the three inner cities," said his father. "See how the Forbidden City shines in the sunlight."

David felt very small, a mere speck in the scene, but at the same time very big. Did he not belong to this? Everyone had his place in the universe, so his Chinese teacher had told him. "I am a Peking man," he said proudly. "Do I have not to be?" He began to cry.

Then his father had taken him in his arms and paced up and down the broad space and around the bastion of the gatehouse. Bit by bit he had learned David's story. After it was told, he had said to his son, "Together we'll take care of Mother. Suppose we don't bother her with our thoughts. I wouldn't say anything to her about being a Peking man. Tell me about it if you like." After a pause he had added, "The trip to America would be too hard for your mother just now. We must see that she does not take it." So it was settled, there was no need to worry. He and his father would take care of Mother and Mother and he would stay right here in Peking.

That night he had been awakened by the voices of his parents coming from the adjacent room (the partitions in Chinese houses are thin, a fact his parents had evidently forgotten that night). David heard his mother cry out, "Please take us home before it's too late. China is beginning to shape David."

"A little, perhaps," said his father, "but is that bad?"

"Surely it's bad. Amah spoils him, so do the other servants."

"I'll keep him more with me," his father had answered.

"Do you think that is going to help? Do you know what he said to me when he came to bid me goodnight? I was talking to him about this morning's verse and what the secret place of the Most High meant and he answered that you had let him look down on the secret place this afternoon, but he couldn't go inside. It was forbidden to look at God."

"That's a child's idea. He'll outgrow it."

"Not unless he goes home, John. The first seven years shape the man. You have no right to commit David to China and to its suffering. Besides, he may not want to serve China as you do. When he plays with amah's children he invents all the games and all the mischief but he sees that they take the punishment. The Chinese may not always like him."

"My dear, my dear, you see China as sinister. It's my fault, I know. I filled you with my own apprehensions. I made it seem sinister to you that time years ago when I brought my troubles to you so suddenly. I've so often regretted it. But now, can't you see, China isn't sinister. New forces are coming in. It's thrilling to be a part of the change that's coming to such an old country."

His mother had cried out, "If you won't take us home, I must go alone, John. It would be hard alone." For a moment David had been angry with his father. Weren't they going to take care of his mother together, he and his father? Not make it hard for her. Then he understood. His father was trying to care for his mother by keeping her in China, but she wouldn't let him.

"John, I love you," he had heard his mother say. "It is because I love you that I persist. It is a strange thing, John, I have always leaned upon you except in this one matter— and even in this, it's as if I draw my strength from you to oppose you. Oh, John, John, a woman is especially sensitive to any danger that may touch those she loves. I sense something you do not. Once you asked for my woman's intuition. Now, when it does not suit you, you cast it aside."

"Emily, I'll do anything I can to make you happy." It was his father speaking again. "I love you, but you won't believe it unless I let you do with me what you want. But even if you should take David away from me, I must stay."

"I cannot reach you, John. If I cannot save you, I must act to save David from this country."

"Very well," said his father.

David clutched the bedclothes, too frightened to move. His father had promised to make his mother understand that he, David, belonged to China! His father wasn't going to help him after all. Only God could help now. He couldn't go into God's city and talk to him personally, but he could speak to him from afar. Slowly he had let go the covers, climbed out of his bed and knelt by its side. "Please, God," he prayed, "don't let Mother take me away. Let her not be *too* strong."

And then there was amah leaning over him. "Shao Con, you not sleep. You listen too much. You stay in China. Amah know. You listen my say."

In the morning when he went to his mother's room he took her his most precious possession, a broken bit of a yellow phoenix that had once adorned the upswung roof of the watchtower of the Forbidden City. His father had picked it up out of the dust of the road and given it to him. She let him sit on her bed, an unusual privilege, and she told him stories she had never told him before, about the clear stream where she went fishing as a little girl.

"I've never fished," he said.

"You will," she answered, "for the stream is near your grandfather's house."

"When I'm big—I'm just a little boy now. I'll be your bracelet," he said to beguile her. When he clasped her arm, fingers and thumb had met. "See," he cried, "I really am a bracelet." Then she had flung her arms around him and held him close. "We must hurry, darling."

A child's imaginings and memories? Only in part. He could not have understood the conversation in the night between his father and mother, let alone remember so much of it. He had found the conversation, carefully recorded, among his father's papers after his death—a man's tormented memory. "What have I done to you, my darling, my frail, beautiful Emily? I have at last told you that I mean to spend my life in China. You want to take David away to America. But I know you aren't strong enough to go without me, not with that furiously beating heart. So I win in the long battle to have my son follow in my footsteps, help in the progress of a great country. Speaking the language like a native, understanding Chinese thought as I never can, he will be the perfect instrument to bring the East and West together. Oh, Emily, Emily."

His mother fought with all her frail strength to keep her son from commitment to China, and he and the servants were silently joined in efforts to keep her from doing so. Harmony between his mother and the servants had been lost on the night of his birth. China has her own ways of aligning herself against those who do not trust her. None of the servants could ever seem to find him when his mother called him to their daily visits designed to entrance him with the fascinating things he could do in America. When she did succeed in getting him to sit with her, the same allies, amah and the houseboy, would scheme for interruptions in the talks. A curio dealer would arrive with especially beautiful old bronzes—of course Madam wanted the most beautiful objects to take to America. The tailor would unexpectedly arrive with garments to be fitted for the journey. Although there was a continual bustle of preparation about the house, it didn't seem to get anywhere.

Then had come that awful day of his mother's death. His father was sitting in his study, his arm around David, talking to the doctor's wife. "I should have left my work and taken her home. She begged me to."

"Don't blame yourself, John. You know, and I think she really did, too, that she was better off here. Where would she have found the tender care the servants have lavished upon her?"

"I wish I could think so."

"Besides, she couldn't have stood the trip."

"Earlier, perhaps."

"Be sensible, John. Her sickness had nothing to do with being in China."

"It might have."

David had sobbed hysterically.

"Let me take him for a day or two," begged the doctor's wife. "It will be good for him to play with my youngsters."

They thought he didn't understand. "Children can't comprehend death," the doctor said when David romped and shouted with an abandonment he had never displayed before. "I am the leader. People do what I want them to," he cried to the doctor's children. "Follow me!" He took them through a lily pond. Their feet wet and muddy, accepting his lead, they romped through the house, giggling and shouting. At the kitchen window he commanded each to make a face at the cook.

Suddenly his amah had swooped down upon him, seized him by the shoulder. "What thing you do, Shao Con, your Mama die, you laugh, you make trouble. No proper son. You break the dauli."

His freedom had been short-lived. So had been his escape from the belief that he had not taken care of his mother.

Longing now as before to escape from his failure to protect her, he left the prow of the junk and joined a knot of sailors. He felt boisterous as he had on that long-ago day. "I'll tell you a tale," he said, addressing them in their own dialect. He would make them laugh and he would laugh with them. "Listen," he cried, "I'll tell you of a foreigner who took off his head to please a Chinese crowd."

There was a loud guffaw.

"Why not?" he demanded. "He'd taken out his teeth for them. Why not unscrew his head?" He moved to show them how.

At the second loud guffaw from the boatmen, Mu San appeared in the doorway of the cabin, a broad grin on his face. He laughed at the boatmen's earthy suggestions about how a man could be further taken apart—details which with gusto they added to David's story. He had spent much of his childhood in his mother's quarters. He had taken part in many a squabble between his peasant mother and her servants, and he had enjoyed the rough humor of the people. The women fanning the charcoal fires under the kettles of rice gruel for the morning repast joined in the laughter.

One of the boatmen, sitting gloomily apart, spoke. "The Reds take men to pieces. My eldest brother was dismembered, part by part, then he died."

Instantly the men's hilarity was silenced. The laodah came among them and spat and swore, cursing the Communists who now patrolled the shore and made piracy difficult and had driven away the wind. He cursed them with barrenness to the fifth and sixth generations. Mu San turned and went back to the cabin. David was bewildered. Trying to escape into comedy, he had simply plunged into the quivering center of China's tragic struggle.

Suddenly the laodah moved his head and sniffed the air, looked at the clouds gathering on the horizon although overhead the sky was blue. He shouted commands to furl the sails, dump the fire in the charcoal stoves under the rice kettles into the sea. The stoves were carried inside. The women gathered up their children and were gone into their cabins. Before the boatmen could furl the mainsail, it was filled with wind and rent in two. Straining and pulling, they brought down the flapping sections.

David hurried up the steps. Clinging to whatever he could, he reached the cabin. Mu San, standing in the doorway, stretched out his hand and drew David within. All at once the junk lurched and flung them against each other. With difficulty they righted themselves.

The laodah took the tiller, swung it hard over, heading

the prow of the junk into the rising wind. He shouted a second order. Two boatmen, clinging like cats to the pitching deck, reached the laodah and lashed him to the rudderpost. Again he bellowed an order, this time to his passengers, "Shut the cabin door."

"My father hired this junk," shouted Mu San. "You cannot order me!" Then the rain and the wind struck him, knocking him against David. Pushing him aside, David closed the door and slid fast the wood bolt that held it in place.

Mu San, searching for his flashlight, stumbled over his servant huddled on the floor, tried to kick him into action, but it was of no use. The man was too sick to rise. A violent lurch of the junk threw David and Mu San to their knees. Loose articles tumbled against them. Groping about in the dark, they finally found the flashlight. They wedged the two stools into a narrow corner where the cabin fitted the junk's stern. In the space behind they dropped the other objects. Then crawling onto their pallets they clutched the handholds fastened to the cabin's sides. As the riotous sea heaved the junk high, dropped it, spun it around, Mu San retched, moaned.

David, listening to the wind's rising to hurricane strength, his whole body shaken by each shudder that passed through the junk when a wave slapped its side, knew no such elation as he had experienced in the freighter's combat with such violence. Then he had felt the power of a good mechanism augmenting man's limited strength. Now only the irregular rude planks out of which the junk—centuries old in design and God knew how many years old in use—

107

was made separated him from the sea, dangerously violent; only puny man lashed to the rudderpost held them away from the rocks along the coast. Between gusts of wind the faint creak of the tiller was audible, then the roar of sea and wind drowned it out. He felt tossed like an infant on the black knees of the sea.

At last, drugged by motion and sound, he dozed. In that half-state between sleeping and wakefulness he was drawn back into his turbulent past. It heaved him high, dropped him, spun him around—revolution, which in his youth had lifted him on foamy crests of idealism, then plunged him down into surging waters, boiling up from the dark and troubled depths of men's souls. Long-forgotten events crowded his mind: October, 1911, rebels victorious in the South demanded the abdication of the Manchus. The night the news reached Peking he, although nine years old, was moved for safety into his father's bedroom.

Fear giving place to relief, to joy. Without bloodshed, the Son of Heaven was dethroned and a president installed in the Forbidden City, democracy established in the wink of an eye. Although the apex of Chinese civilization was gone, for a time the corners of the universe were upheld by farmers and scholars, merchants and soldiers. But slowly forces of evil, lying dormant under the stale usage of centuries, were let loose. Greedy men saw their opportunity, gathered armies together, crisscrossed the country, collected taxes years in advance. Merchants again and again bought their lives with huge donations to one warlord after another. Peasants were forced to grow opium to finance them. The scholars who had ruled the provinces were replaced by these brigands. Chaotic years when he and his father were drawn deeper and deeper into China's struggles passed like a kaleidoscope before David's eyes.

Then from the turbulent past David was again in the turbulent present. A sudden lurch of the junk, and Mu San's grasp on the handhold gave way. He was thrown against David, who quickly reached over the limp figure and grasped the handhold Mu San had let slip, binding the two together to resist the storm's buffeting.

Lack of food, the ceaseless tossing, the roar of the winds, the waves mounting and breaking over the junk, gradually produced in David a trancelike state. Feeling the slightness of young Chen's body against his own, he had the illusion that he was young again, filled with the enthusiasm of youth. He was in Peking. He was the proud companion of his beloved father, fifteen, mature beyond his years, his father said, old enough now to enter the Middle School at the Chinese university.

The arrival—stepping out of his ricksha into the bare grounds of the university, he walked by his father's side among the Chinese boys, no longer effeminate looking, masculine with their cropped hair, their foreign shoes. And girls, some very gay, "All same Americans." Boys and girls, eager to be modern.

Then, out of them all, one boy stood out clearly. He was gayer, freer than all the rest—Lo was his name. He was not built like the Northerners, but slight and agile, a Southerner, his mind as quick as the movements of his body. David dubbed him "the fawn" for there was a fawn-like look about him—an effect created by his slightly pointed ears, pointed chin, broad forehead topped by jet-black hair standing stiffly up. A lively curiosity danced in his black eyes, often all but destroying the serenity of the classic Chinese scholar, still cultivated by students.

They called each other friend, and Lo came often with a group of students to John Conway's house to discuss democracy. They argued, they disagreed. They swung high on fabulous wings of hope—salvation lay in Western techniques; they despaired—their culture was old-fashioned but how difficult it was to get rid of it! His father's face was in shadow; his hands clasped together, resting on his desk, were within the circle of light cast by the oil lamp. And he was speaking of the dignity of labor, the basis of democracy. "Things you make with your hands are important—ships, railroads—but they must not be an end in themselves. Only since I came to your country have I realized that material progress has its dangers. Against those dangers you must preserve what Sir Francis, the Englishman so revered by your scholars, calls the 'talismanic jewel.' Guard it, never let it be destroyed."

"Talismanic jewel." Lo repeated the phrase. "It is like poetry," he suddenly exclaimed, his eyes bright with interest. "The meaning?"

And when David's father translated the words as best he could into Chinese, Lo murmured, "A charm—charms are used against devils." Again Lo's laughter of so long ago seemed to echo around David in the dark confines of the junk. Into the laughter came his father's quiet voice, "A mechanized life can be evil, Lo, unless against it you place your philosophy that the creative in man lies in harmony—shall I say of opposites? The cultures of East and West are the opposites—a creative force if brought into harmony."

Silence. David was startled. Would they be offended? The dividing of the world into male and female was not spoken of openly. Deep and secret the Chinese held this idea of the universe. Bit by bit it had been revealed to David by his Chinese teacher, his amah, who after his mother's death had seen to it that he lived as much as possible in the Chinese world.

"Our tools are what they want to know about." Hastily David injected these words into the silence, for he, like the Chinese, partook of the necessity to treasure in secrecy this knowledge of the world's creative power through male and female.

Now the subject was changed—the boys sought advice about the separate family, about giving up concubinage, about love before marriage, about choosing their mates. Like many Westerners teaching Western individualism, David's father, although captivated by China's philosophy, at the same time was destroying it for these boys. David, sensing the paradox, was troubled. Out of the years his father appeared and *he* seemed to be troubled—these youths' acceptance of the West was too close to worship, too blind an adoration of Christendom. Could Christendom measure up?

Little by little David's apprehensions faded. East and West were the opposites needed in a perfect world, his world, where he and Lo were the perfect friends. Amah ruled the house and most of the time its two occupants. Seasons came and went and life was good.

Now David's memory scooped out a new channel. He now seemed to be in the midst of a blinding summer sun which lay upon a silt-laden river flowing sluggishly within its dykes. His father, appearing older and a little stooped, was supervising a group of students, David and Lo among them, in a surveying project on the lower reaches of the Yellow River. Sweat broke out on David's back and legs as he lifted to his shoulders the heavy tripod with its mounted telescope, but with bravado he carried it from the flat fields to the top of the dyke and down again. Lo climbed more slowly but sturdily, insisting on carrying his own equipment, but when they came to a village Lo shirked the task, pretending to be an overseer. David felt scornful of his friend for reverting to the traditional conception that labor was beneath a student.

On a holiday the two boys wandered off by themselves, and Lo read aloud scenes from *The Dream of the Red Chamber* and another novel, the title of which did not come back to David, although his confusion over the erotic scenes of men and their concubines seemed very real, even now. Lo understood and enjoyed what embarrassed his friend. And then, out of that summertime, David heard distinctly Lo's beautiful voice, its musical intonations, as he read from the ancient poets. To the wild rhythm of the storm David now began softly chanting with Lo the beautiful images—"fallen moonlight, temple of immensity, precipice of life."

Autumn, and they were back in Peking. The air in its

lightness was akin to the lightness of their bodies. Closer friends than ever, the two boys strolled through the outer courts of the Forbidden City, open to the public since the establishment of democracy. Across the marble bridges, around the lakes they strolled, forever talking of what they would do for China.

Lo was wearing his first foreign suit, made by a local tailor. The collar yawned, the trousers were too short. It was brown, heavy English tweed. David's suit also was made by the local tailor, and it also fitted him badly. But they felt themselves modern and a little superior.

Startled out of his dreams, David was once more in the present. How long he had held Mu San he did not know, but his hand, numbed by strain, had suddenly let go the handgrip and Mu San was thrown from him. He sought to draw the slight figure back into his embrace, but Mu San, roused to consciousness by his sudden release, held himself away, and so it seemed to David did Lo, his boyhood friend, so close to him a moment before.

The interlude of the bright summer and the companionship were gone. In Chinese eyes, even Lo's, David and his father had lost face. Had not he and his father held before the Chinese the ideals of democracy, only to find that Christianity did not practice what it preached? It was 1917 and America had entered the first World War. Idle for David to try to explain that he was not responsible for America's entrance into the war. Lo was disappointed in him—and America.

Now, lying separate from his companion, David sought

to lose himself again in the illusion that he was young, but no longer did he feel the identification with his youth and with his friend Lo as he had when he had held Mu San in his embrace. He was a grown man, now embarked on a dangerous mission, searching his past for guidance. And yet it was the very next summer that he had visited Lo at his home, a thing few Westerners were ever asked to do. Friendship with Westerners, yes, but let it not lead to intimacy with the family.

Surprised and delighted at his invitation, David was wholly content when his father had consented to the plan, seeing in the summer an opportunity for David to close the breach between the two boys made by America's entrance into the war. At first, as in the previous summer, there was sunlight and friendship and the glorious sense of sharing as from the deck of the steamer they looked out on the broad stretches of the Yangtse. David noted with secret satisfaction that whether he looked up the river or down he saw steamers of Western nations, American among them. But he said nothing of this to Lo, sensitive over Western control of so much of his country's shipping, lest he disturb the good relationship between them so recently reestablished.

Together they had left the steamer at the upriver port where Lo's family had lived for centuries; together in sedan chairs they rode through the city streets; together they passed through the gate of his ancestral home. There the chairs were lowered from the shoulders of the chairbearers and David stood within the closely guarded privacy of a Chinese family.

"The master awaits the young master," bowing, the gateman spoke. Other servants stretching in a line across the court bowed, and spoke their greetings. "Young master, welcome!" But for David there were only stares. Had they never seen a white man before? Embarrassed, he followed Lo across a court to a doorway before which hung a bamboo curtain. Lifting it, Lo ushered his friend into the presence of an elderly man seated by a table at the end of a narrow room.

"Thy unworthy son has returned," said Lo, "and with him is his honorable friend."

After the formalities were over, Lo led David through a narrow corridor and into a smaller court, set apart from the main ones. Opening a door, he stood aside for his friend to enter. "This is my court," said Lo, "make yourself comfortable. I beg you to accept my apology for a short absence. I must go to my mother. The servants will bring you water for bathing. When you have bathed, if you clap your hands they will bring you food. Again my apology."

"No need for apology. It is to keep the custom you go," David replied. "I understand the custom of your people that I do not go with you into the women's quarters."

Leisurely David went about taking the bath prepared for him in a deep green tub, shaped like a giant flowerpot, standing in an alcove adjoining one of the smaller rooms. He dressed, and making himself at home, as Lo had told him, he began exploring. At each end of the room were doors. Opening one of them he found himself in what looked like a bridal chamber, for it held a bridal bed with red trappings, embroidered with symbols of fertility. Hastily he shut the door.

A moment later two menservants entered and placed three bowls of food on a table under the window—a simple meal such as the family was probably eating, thought David. But the attendance upon him was careless and the dishes designed to be hot were only moderately so. Wise in the ways of the Chinese, David began to suspect that something was amiss. Was he not welcome? Could it be that he was not expected, not even wanted? Surely Lo would not do such a thing; he would not wish to humiliate his friend, and certainly not to be welcome was to be humiliated. Never before had David been the object of such an indirect insult from a Chinese friend. He decided, when Lo returned, to find out what was wrong.

Hour after hour he waited. Finally he fell asleep, his head resting on his arms stretched across the table. He was aroused by Lo's entrance; he was carrying clean writing brushes and paper. Solemnly he placed himself opposite David at the table, then asked David if he would pledge in blood his loyalty to the New China and to their friendship. David at first held back from a rite which seemed to him too primitive, but finally he had consented. Lo showed him how to open the vein in his wrist. Then, using the clean brushes, they wrote their vows in blood—an act which left David a little shaken, but again warm in his belief in his friend.

But he was a friend who, as the days went by, seemed less and less familiar. Lo's laughter, heretofore so much a part of him, was gone, so also was his curiosity and his vigor. Half the day he lounged in his own quarters, evincing no desire to show his friend the city about which he had talked so much. David was both disappointed and bored. He kept thinking of the good companionship with Lo of the summer before.

"I'd like to see the country around here."

"So you don't like the way we live," Lo retorted.

"I didn't say that."

"But you meant it," Lo, now dropping all Eastern evasiveness together with the politeness of his people, shot back at him. "Why should we do anything? It's the hottest month of the year. Do, do, you always want to be *doing!* The trouble with you," he went on, "is that you have a romantic idea about me. You want me always to act like one of our old scholars, wear my black scholar's gown."

"Romantic," stormed David. "You who call a dirty alley the *Street of the Seven Delights*. What about the hovels in the *Street of Seven Delights*, the children covered with boils? Maybe that's why you don't take me around, you don't want me to see things like that."

"What about your beatitudes? Your country has been fighting just as if you had never heard of Christ," Lo flung back.

They quarreled that evening.

"I think I'd better leave," said David.

"You can't. You've pledged yourself to me. I need you." Lo said it simply and David believed him; but in what way his friend needed him he did not comprehend.

Bored and often lonely, for Lo now began disappearing

for hours at a time, David decided to see the city for him-self. The streets were narrow, not like the broad ones of Peking. The hot, humid air hung like an exhaust sucking up David's vitality. No wonder Lo didn't want to leave the cool courts of his ancestral home where the great paving stones were wetted down every few hours, David told himself in justification of his friend's behavior. Leaving the narrow streets behind, David sought out the waterfront. He was fascinated. He began to take an enormous pride in the Western world, which he found dominated the shipping business. There was an air of excitement upon each steamer's departure for the turbulent, dangerous stretch of the upper river full of rapids and whirlpools that led through the gorges to the hinterland. He caught snatches of talk by captains, by pilots coming off their runs or starting upon the exciting, perilous journey.

For days he tried to make up his mind to go to the foreign club, where he had learned these men gathered. Finally, conquering shyness and a feeling of awkwardness, one afternoon he quietly pushed open the door, stood just inside, unnoticed, looking at the room full of men. All had their coats off, their shirts open; their bodies were taut with energy. Some were sitting silent playing cards; some, who were standing at the bar, were talking the jargon of the shipping business. He heard owners and captains gloating over the power of their engines, which took ships over the rapids without calling upon the Chinese trackers to help them. There was no need to throw out the cables to coolies to pull them over the rapid head. Let the trackers curse them for taking away their rice. Machinery was efficiency.

These Westerners belonged to the river and to work. Energy seemed to leap up in the room, pulling at unused reservoirs in David. Sounds of the river, the dropping of anchor chains, the coolies' chants as they loaded or unloaded cargo drifted across the room.

As quietly as he had come, David went out and back to Lo's home and to the court he and his friend occupied. Lo was not there. He threw himself down on the hard Chinese bed and drew the curtains. He wanted to think. He'd get a job on one of the upriver steamers, be a part of the Western man's world of danger and accomplishment. Gradually he became conscious of voices, one of them Lo's, the other a woman's, coming from the direction of the room he had entered that first night when he had discovered what he believed to be a bridal chamber.

Lo was not talking the classical language of the educated now, but the dialect of this part of the country, intelligible to David only if he listened closely. Hearing his own name and also the term "foreign devil" spoken by the woman, he gave his attention to understanding what they were saying.

"Each day since you returned I eat bitterness. I no longer have dignity even before your father's concubine. She has two sons, and they obey her, but you, my only son, the rightful son, refuse to carry on the family." Her voice was raised in anger.

"I simply want to choose my wife. I want an educated girl who will be a companion to me," Lo pleaded.

"Unfilial son, you would disgrace me in the eyes of the honorable family whose daughter has been pledged in marriage to you."

"You would have me stay in this house and be defiled with this opium traffic that my father's sons, two and three, find so profitable? Opium, a curse that has been placed upon our family," Lo answered.

"It is you who defile me, bringing one of the foreign devils into the very rooms that were prepared for you and your bride. You defile me, and you defile yourself and the family. It is not enough that these foreign devils live in this city and control the life of our Great River. Don't think because I live in the women's courts I don't know what these foreign devils have done to us with their talk of democracy—the Son of Heaven replaced by warlords who have taxed this honorable family until it is forced to deal in opium. Where does the money for your education come from—education that teaches you to defy your mother? For two hundred years we've tried to keep these foreign devils out."

David listened to the words pouring from Lo's mother as only they could pour from an irate Chinese woman. Then he heard Lo say, "Honorable mother, your unworthy son does not wish to defile the honorable house of his father. Let it be compromise between us. Your unworthy son will fulfill the promises made by you and my honorable father in my childhood. I will marry the woman. When a son is born, let your unworthy son depart and continue his learning."

"Only if the foreign devil leaves the house of your ancestors can you be married. Would you have bad luck descend upon us?"

"I will try to arrange that he leave," said Lo.

David rose and stole quietly out of the house. At the shipping offices he booked his passage home.

Two days later on a hot morning Lo and his father stood with their guest on the deck of the downriver steamer. Over and over Lo lamented his friend's going.

Over and over David answered, "This is a parting that is unbearable to me, but my honorable father's frailty demands his son's presence." For the first time the hollow, meaningless phrases, demanded by Chinese politeness, he was uttering revolted David. John Conway was as strong as an ox! And both Lo and he knew David was going because it no longer served Lo's purpose to have his friend with him. For an hour, while the ship was searched for hidden opium, they continued to exchange courtesies, but at last it was over. The gong for departure sounded. Lo and his father walked down the gangplank, stood on the shore in the blazing sun, bowing in farewell.

When he could see them no longer, David went down to the dining saloon and with relief ate his lunch among his own countrymen. "Democracy," the man sitting at his left scoffed, "what does China care about democracy? Look at these warlords."

"They've got the country carved up between them, all right," a man across the table answered.

"They're sucking the life out of the trade we've brought them," the captain chimed in. "Here we've been tied up for a half day hunting the opium hidden God only knows where. Such delays cost the company thousands each trip."

David, thinking of the conversation between Lo and his mother over opium, wondered if all the time, while Lo's father was murmuring polite farewell phrases to his unwelcome guest, he was secretly enjoying the discomfiture of the foreign shipowners, who were unable to discover where the illicit cargo was hidden—maybe *his* cargo! David felt old in cynicism.

Back in Peking, he would not own that he was lonely without his friend. Angrily he told his father, "I'm through with Lo, even if he does come back."

"If he comes back, surely you'll meet him halfway," pleaded David's father. "Help him. It's his testing time."

"Why did he have to use me and then drop me?" demanded David.

"We taught him to set aside the ancient customs of his people. We've helped to upset him. We can hardly desert him now."

David did not answer, but he began thinking more and more of his own country—what had his mother said about a wise person being detached?

The winter came on, cold and blustery. His father gave him a Mongolian pony. At the thieves' market he bought himself a falcon. The day after, a high wind laden with dust from the Gobi Desert swept down from the north and David, with the falcon on his wrist, rode his pony through the dust-veiled city, shadowed by the dim watchtowers of its gates, their upflung roofs rising out of the dust-saturated air like the enormous wings of mythical animals. He raised his arm, with the hooded bird clasping the leather gauntlet bound about his wrist. In fantasy he was one of the gentry of medieval days—trappings of the East borrowed to make him forget that he did not belong to the Chinese world he had espoused as his.

And then he was no longer set apart. China became a partner in the war that was shaking Christendom. Again East and West had found a meeting ground; David was again accepted.

Chapter 7

HE DID NOT STOP TO QUESTION
the ephemeral nature of this acceptance. His eyes saw
only a New China emerging. Good was coming out of
the evil of war—more communication between East and
West. Forgetting he meant to remain detached, he was
swept up into the enthusiasm of students and professors
for the imaginative new program which more and more
was claiming the attention of the elite. The language of the
common people was to take the place of the literary language; a Chinese renaissance would follow. Magazines
sprang up. It was new youth, new everything. The dead
hand of the past must be lifted from learning; the old

rituals, the old philosophies must go—Buddhism, Confucianism, Taoism must be swept away; the new society must be based on efficiency and science—democracy, communism must be given a hearing. The philosophies of Western governments hung in the balance that winter. Social reform began to be talked about. David felt identified with the throbbing new life.

His father kept urging a sober understanding of the meaning of democracy—not an elite who would rule, but dedicated men and women infiltrating the villages and towns of China slowly, carefully teaching the people social and economic democracy. Thus the people would gradually come to a new way of life without breaking violently with the old traditions.

One day in the university library, John Conway had pointed out to his son an older student who was employed to carry newspapers to students sitting at the tables—a menial task in the eyes of the Chinese. He was slightly built. Like Lo, obviously a Southerner. Unlike most of the boys, who were well groomed, even elegant in their black student gowns, he was shabby, his gown worn at the cuffs and gray from many washings. He was thin, almost emaciated. "Mao Tse-tung is his name. He has a fine mind. I've seen some of his papers. I wish he'd enroll in one of my classes, but I fear he never will. I'd like to explain democracy to him," said David's father. "I understand he has the Chinese scholar's traditional disdain for the West. Although he comes from a peasant family, he is well trained in the Confucian doctrines. I wish I could get hold of him."

David was silent, not wishing to tell his father what he

knew about this young man: that he was bitterly opposed to the Confucian precepts which had been drilled into him by his father; that he bitterly resented the introduction of Christianity into China; that he considered John Conway an intruder in a Chinese university and that he despised the rich students whom he served and the professors who ignored him. He had come north from the province of Hunan with a group of students who were destined to sail for Europe to help the Allies. In return for their manual labor they would receive Western education, but Mao had only used the trip north to get to Peking. He had no desire to absorb Western culture; he wanted to be a scholar in the traditional Chinese sense. He was examining the Western philosophies of government simply to find out what it was that made the West powerful. He had discarded one after another, democracy, socialism, anarchism. Communism held his interest at present, and he had organized a group of students to study Marx. This much David had learned about Mao Tse-tung from other students. David, like his father, wished he might know this strangely fascinating peasant with the brilliant eyes who was being talked of more and more by the students, but he, the son of the American, was no more acceptable to Mao Tse-tung than the father.

In the blackness above him David, lying on his pallet clutching the handhold, saw the face of Mao Tse-tung enlarged many times as in the pictures of him seen everywhere in Shanghai after the Communists came in. His face was no longer thin but plump, but the eyes were brilliant with inner fire, as they had been in his youth. David asked himself now, why had Mao discarded the thinking of England and America, more in harmony with his conception of the cultivated man than that of Russia? Russia, with its history of violence, suppression and aggression, had always been a threat to China. If Mao hated the West, why had he not used his creative mind to revitalize Chinese thinking instead of forcing the individualistic Chinese into the pattern of collective man?

Too cold and weary for such reflection, David tried to put Mao Tse-tung out of his mind. The winds and the rain and the pounding of the waves making a barrier, shutting him off from Mao Tse-tung, David lapsed again into dreams of his youth. The winter when he was seventeen had brought him his first love. Down the street lived a member of parliament. Quite unexpectedly he had invited David and his father to a feast at his home. "What is to be desired is compromise between Eastern and Western ideas," he said as they sat down to the feast. "Compromise is the reason for our survival these many centuries. Today my wife and my daughter will join us for the last course—in accordance with your custom that the two sexes mingle at a feast."

Vividly, as on that day, David saw her—dressed in sober black short jacket and neat black trousers, her hair was not short like that of girls he knew at the university, but drawn back, glistening and smooth, into a long braid, her face calm, according to ancient custom: she was beautiful in the way of Chinese women in the ancient paintings, exquisite, quiet, delicate movements of hands, body, downcast eyes. For the first time in his life, he was in love. He was in real despair; he would never see her again although she lived two gates down the street. Then the miracle had happened. The member of parliament, it seemed, had invited them for a purpose. It was a feast of arrangement—would John Conway tutor his daughter? He desired Western learning for his daughter, but not the freedom of the West.

Truly wonderful months for David. There was the cold, windy ride on his pony across the city to his classes at the university, where he drank in the heady wine of new thought, then the ride home in the winter afternoon—the flap of his fur cap drawn up over his face with only a small opening for his eyes, through which he looked out at the muffled figures skirting close to the walls of houses and shops, seeking protection from the wind. The iron-rimmed wheels of the carts revolving on the frozen streets sent out metallic sounds. The sun, sinking low, touched the medieval city with mystery. He urged his pony on. He would be happy if he could catch only a glimpse of the girl, Phoenix, who came daily to his father's study!

To his command the gate of his father's house would swing open. Striding across the court, he entered the warm central room of the house, waited there for Phoenix and her amah to cross the court from his father's study. The slight feminine figure was all but lost in her padded winter garments, but her face, her finely chiselled, aristocratic features, her expression lovelier than ever under his father's prodding of her mind, filled his dreams. To worship her at a distance was enough.

In the spring, when the new leaves of the willows embroidered the stylized pattern of the four cities with delicate greenery, David's happiness was made complete, for one evening Lo, without explanation, came with other students to talk to John Conway. He offered no apology for his treatment of David during the summer. He simply took for granted that David was still his friend and that they would again spend much time together.

"I intend to give myself fully to the New China," he had said. "This," waving his hand, designating the circular white marble Altar of Heaven where they had gone for an afternoon's outing, "this is antiquated. There is no Son of Heaven to report to Heaven on the performance of his heavenly-assigned duties."

As he spoke, the two young men in their heavy foreign shoes walked up the shallow marble steps leading to the first marble terrace, crossed it, took the steps to the second, and then to the third—the circular marble-floored empty space where previously the accounting to Heaven had been made. Since democracy had been declared in China, the enclosure had been open to the public and David had come here often with his father. Today he was stirred by the simple dignity of the altar and saddened over its neglect. Some of the rounded marble posts carved with dragons, set at intervals in the marble railings edging the three terraces, already were broken. The long avenues bordered by tall cypresses, which led to the altar, were choked with grass.

"My father says there's no such impressive place of worship anywhere else in all the world as this. Its being open to the sky is what makes it so."

Lo shrugged. "It's old-fashioned." He stopped, picked up a bit of marble fallen from one of the railings and tossed it into the weeds at the foot of the altar.

To David the wind sounded mournful, sighing through the cypress trees. "Let's go," he said. Silently the two left the enclosure. But when they were part way down the avenue of cypress trees he made his friend turn and look back at the altar. "It may be old-fashioned but it's beautiful," he insisted.

And Lo, who loved beauty, stood for a long time looking at it. "That's what Mao would say."

Always Mao, thought David, a little enviously, for Lo was one of the group the peasant scholar had drawn about him. David, a Westerner, was not acceptable. But how had it happened that the obscure Mao had so quickly gained influence over Lo? More and more Mao was drawing young men to him.

When they parted that afternoon Lo said, "I wish to break with the tradition of feudalism. A man's duty is first to himself." Feudalism was the new catchword used by the young to express their disapproval of traditional family ties. David felt certain this reference to it was Lo's way of explaining what had happened. He had bowed to the decree of his family and had married the old-fashioned girl, the choice of his parents, and stayed until a son was born. Fortunate that it was a son or Lo wouldn't be here had been David's somewhat cynical reaction. Still, Lo had broken with the family and he needed David, but did he need him more than he needed Mao?

Once, walking through the outer courts of the Forbidden City, they passed Mao. He had let his hair grow long and it hung about his ears. He was incredibly thin.

"You talk so much about him, but he didn't speak to you," said David.

"I think he was absorbed in his thoughts," Lo replied.

David, seeing how ill at ease his friend was, understood. You know why he didn't speak, he was about to say, it's because you are with a foreigner, and then he kept still, for he didn't want to quarrel with his friend so recently restored to him.

"Mao's in love with the daughter of our philosophy professor," said Lo. "He's a friend of all our thinkers, but he thinks for himself. He's dedicated to learning. He's the perpetual student. He reads poetry half the time."

"Dedicated to poetry at this time. And you admire him when China is trying to become modern," scoffed David, and then was sorry.

"He's dedicated to China," Lo answered with dignity. "He's visited every imperial monument in Peking. He's walked clear around the city wall."

"So have we," David countered.

"He's leaving soon. He's going to make a pilgrimage to all the historic sites of China," said Lo, ignoring David's last remark.

"I don't see why you are so impressed by him," answered David, refusing to be impressed himself. But their differences did not separate them as in the summer.

There were exciting events taking place in Peking and the two were involved in the secret plans students were making. They were angry at both their own diplomats and those of other countries. At the peace table China had been sold out; a whole Chinese province had been given to Japan for her part in the war, nothing given to China for her part. The students must act, since the officials had not.

Chapter 8

ONE SATURDAY MORNING IN May David had been awakened by the sun shining through the windows of his room. Still drowsy, he had lain for some time thinking of the part he was to play in tomorrow's parade. But what was he to do in the interim to hold down his impatience? Gradually a plan took shape in his mind. This was the day of the month for the thieves' market held in the grounds of a nearby temple. He thought he might find there a fitting present for Phoenix which would be within reach of his pocketbook. He might by this means break down the old-fashioned barriers which had been erected between him and the girl.

When he entered the market he found the place already crowded and the noise of many bargains filling the air. He felt delight in the scene as he passed among the booths and picked his way among the humble dealers whose wares were spread out on bits of blue cloth on the ground. Sir Francis, the friend of his father, standing before a bookstall, stopped his bargaining long enough to greet his friend's son. Ahead of him, David could see the familiar broad back of the doctor's wife. Wishing to avoid the kindly woman who would undoubtedly want to help him with his errand he slipped down a side alley.

Ahead of him was the stall where last winter he had bought his falcon. He hesitated for a little before a parrot with a beautiful rose-colored breast. "Very fine bird, very cheap," said the vendor, recognizing his former customer. David started to lift the parrot's feathers. The owner moved the bird out of reach. A plump Chinese woman standing nearby laughed. "David," she jeered. The owner shrugged. David walked on.

Then before him he saw the perfect present—a dwarf peach tree standing in a bowl at the temple's steps. Feigning indifference, he offered a small purchasing price.

"Ai yah, you would rob me," cried the flower vendor.

"That tree has no roots. It will die before I get it home," David retorted.

"Young master, it's a fine tree. I will dig it up from its pot so you can see."

"All you have to do is to yank it. It hasn't any roots. I will give you the value of the blossoms."

"Rob a poor man whose sons go hungry," whined the

vendor, squatting among his pink blossoms and blue pots. "Fifty coppers more and it is yours."

"Thirty." David moved loftily away.

"Forty."

David flung down the money. Each had enjoyed the bargaining. Compromise was good.

As he left the temple grounds, David passed near a group of foreigners. "It's still the old China, isn't it?" said a woman from the American Legation, whom he knew by sight. "There won't be any trouble over the Versailles Treaty, I'm sure."

It may be the old China, but there's a volcano under it! thought David. On the ride home, with his treasure held between his knees so that its delicate blossoms should not be shaken, he put from his mind tomorrow's volcanic eruption—for that it was to be. The tree was beautifully dwarfed. The blossoms hung in exquisite clusters. It was indeed the perfect gift for Phoenix.

"Young master wishes me to lose my job," cried the gateman when David insisted he deliver the little tree. "Son of the honorable teacher who pays my wages, are you my enemy? Why else would you ask me to break the customs of the great house down the street? Trouble, trouble! A peach tree cannot be hidden."

"Say it is from my father," begged David.

"A return will be made, a return present. Questions will be asked by your honorable father. My humble self will be blamed."

David jingled the coins in his pocket. The gateman's

protests grew fainter. "Perhaps I could say from the great family of Con and thus keep the custom."

All evening David hoped for some word from Phoenix; none came.

The next day began in high excitement. He joined Lo and together they went to the appointed place. A crowd of students had already gathered, all talking, all gesticulating. "The Anfu Clique have sold the country out at the Peace Table. They've agreed to give Shantung province to Japan." Japan given Chinese land to repay them for their part in fighting the Germans. Japan, their feared neighbor; China, who had sent thousands of her coolies to help win the war, given nothing; instead a whole province taken from her. "Our officials have sold us out. America has betrayed us! She promised to guard our interests. It's because we are weak. Material strength is all that counts."

Suddenly the students were conscious of David and they cried out against him. But Lo took David's hand and led him deep into the crowd, shouting, "He is my friend!" The ancient custom of friendship held and he, the American, was accepted for Lo's sake. Now the crowd moved forward, sweeping down the main thoroughfare of the city. White banners appeared. "Down with the foreigners! Down with the traitors in our own country! Down with the Anfu men in parliament!" Boys and girls moved forward, joined constantly by others coming in from side streets—Chinese youths, shouting their protest against their leaders who had betrayed the country.

Disillusioned, bitter, angry, thousands strong, their white banners of mourning floating triumphantly above them, they moved like a river in flood down the streets and into the great space before the wall-enclosed house of the Minister of Finance, one of the Anfu Clique. David's heart beat against his chest like a great hammer—he, at last, one with the Chinese youth in their struggle. The square was full, and silent. Across the stillness like the cut of a knife fell the sound of shattering glass. The more daring had scaled the wall which surrounded the Minister's residence. The students had broken into the house! Flames leaped up above the wall, they had dared to set on fire an official's dwelling because officials had failed in their duty to the nation. Nationalism flamed in the hearts of all the students who stood there watching.

And then soldiers on nimble Mongolian ponies rode straight into the crowd. Even now David seemed to hear the sound of the ponies' beating hoofs and the thud of clubs on soft flesh and the cries from within the compound! A student climbed back over the wall! "The soldiers have got our men! Hurry, get away! Get away!" he shouted. The crowd melted like snow under a sudden rain, carelessly scattered as leaves blown about in a wind. David, before he too fled, saw sprawled figures, a boy, a young girl, her short knee-length skirt, indicating defiance of convention, thrown high, her pretty hands still clasping a banner; its white folds lay across her face.

He hurried along the empty streets to his home and his father's protecting presence. Sadly John Conway greeted him. "They think we've betrayed them. It looks as if we have. This is what I feared. Too much blind worship of the West. We offend them when we least intend to."

A sudden violent hammering on the gate sent them hurrying to see who so urgently had sought them out. They saw Phoenix's amah stumping toward them across the court crying, "Ai yah, Ai yah! The master has fled. The daughter would make atonement for her father, an Anfu man. Quickly, quickly, come!"

John Conway hurried after the amah. David, white-faced, followed. "Wait here," commanded his father, and David obeyed, stopping just inside the first court where he could look down a vista of corridors leading from court to court. Had Phoenix been in the crowd of students? Atonement, for what? For a long time he waited.

Then into the court Phoenix stumbled, supported by his father and her amah. Phoenix, always before dainty, composed, exquisite, was weeping and crying out, "Let me atone with my life! My father has betrayed his country! The family should die! Let us be wiped out!" David had never before witnessed such abandonment except among the poor who, in times of bereavement, wailed noisily in the alleyways of Peking. But Phoenix—

The three moved across the sunlit court and disappeared into a room on the other side but the wailing did not cease. "Let me die! There is no other way to wash out my father's guilt. Only in death can the enormity of his crime be erased!"

Gradually the girl's wailing ceased and David saw his father coming toward him. "Don't worry," he said, laying his hand on his son's shoulder. "I think she'll be all right when she wakens. This is the old concept of the solidarity of the family—guilt for one, guilt for all. She

tried to kill herself. We gave her something to quiet her."
David noticed for the first time the disordered court;
clothes strewn about. Had the family fled? Why had
Phoenix not fled with them? In the midst of the disorder
the peach tree stood erect in its blue pot, but it had no
meaning for him now.

When after two days no word had come from the great
house, John Conway sent him to inquire. He found the
gate barred, and there was no answer to his knock. What
had happened to Phoenix neither David nor his father
could learn. He tried again and again to find out from his
own amah. "I no savee," she would answer, but David believed she knew.

A hard and unyielding nationalism now claimed the
students whose mandates even the merchants accepted, im-
posing boycotts on foreign goods. Officials of the government dared not oppose them.

At the university suddenly great concern was shown
for John Conway's health. It was suggested that for the
few weeks remaining in the term he take a leave of absence.

"It's their way of saying they don't want you," David
contended bitterly.

"It's a polite way of saving me the humiliation of finding
an empty classroom," his father answered. "My students
would be called my 'running dogs' if they came to my
classes."

"I am relieving the university of the embarrassment of
my presence. I have resigned," later his father told David.

"To go home!" cried David.

"No, I'll probably join the faculty of one of the missionary schools."

For a moment David had been angry. Did his father have no thought except for China? Was he, too, to be swallowed up in his father's goodness? "In detachment there is wisdom"—those were his mother's words and they made sense.

That was the first time David had noticed that his father was no longer massive, that some indefinable chiselling away of the purely physical by the spirit of this good man had occurred, a process probably going on for many years. He looked spent. He needs me, David thought, and suddenly he was overwhelmed with love for his father. And yet he could not give up his determination to extricate himself from China. He was in his eighteenth year. It was long past time that he see his own country—his own country. Yes, now at last he was ready to acknowledge that America was his own country.

"Couldn't we have a few weeks together in the Western Hills—before I leave for America?" With difficulty he had completed the sentence which informed his father of his intention to leave China.

A few days later they went to the temple, where for many previous summers they had been paying guests of the priests, and there they spent two months together. On the evening before David was to leave, he and his father stood side by side watching the gray-robed priests come out of the shadows. Chanting and clicking the beads of their rosaries, they entered the main temple and knelt before a great golden Buddha. David had impatiently exclaimed, "You know, Father, most of these priests are degenerate. It's absurd for you to be moved by their worship."

"A man worships God, or he worships himself," his father had answered, "and when he worships himself he comes in time to worship the brute in him. However clouded by superstition, there is in this service a recognition of the mystery of God."

"I thought you—" David began.

"Yes, I came as the advocate of a mechanized world. And now I am staying as the advocate of God."

Returning to him now were his father's words: "I do not see clearly what is happening to China, but I have come to believe that if the traditions by which a people have risen are entirely forgotten, men's souls are lost; but if tradition, however good, is held too rigidly, it also corrupts. I think it is the need to save and yet destroy tradition that confuses youths like your friend Lo. I am responsible for some of this confusion. Possibly you—"

David had an imperfect memory of the rest of that night's talk with his father, but the setting was clear—the stone-flagged guest room, a candle between them on the table, a light wind sighing in the pines outside. In the gray dawn, as his father leaned forward to blow out the candle, he had revealed his tired, sad eyes.

Restlessly David sought to throw off the powerful hold memory had upon him, a final memory—his friend Lo coming up to the Hills to wish him a pleasant journey.

Mu San called weakly to his servant for tea, and the man simply groaned in answer. Slowly it penetrated

David's mind that he must minister to Mu San, if he were to be ministered to. Slowly, too, he realized that the junk was tossing less violently and that the wind had lessened in fury enough so that he dared loosen his grip on the handhold. He crawled from his pallet and with the help of Mu San's flashlight found the teapot squeezed in between the stove and a stool. He shook it. There was tea in it. Gently he raised Mu San. Steadying him with his own body, he held the spout to the younger man's lips. Mu San pulled away murmuring polite thanks. David covered the huddled figure, then drank the cold unpalatable tea and lay down again. He shivered under his thin blanket.

Listening to the wind still beating around the cabin, he brooded over the fact that Mu San, despite their joint undertaking, had not accepted from him even the offering of a cup of tea. It would be futile to try to rescue Damon, he decided. He could not go through with the undertaking without a friend to help him.

He fell into a heavy sleep. When he woke there was silence all around him. The junk was bobbing about on a choppy sea. The storm was spent. Half suffocated by the fetid air of the cabin, he slid back the bolt and opened the door a crack. A burst of fresh air swept in. He turned, looking down on his companion. What had *he* been dreaming or thinking of during those long hours? Suddenly Mu San cried out and David turning saw his companion draw his legs up to his chest in a convulsive movement, his face contorted. Suddenly he threw himself forward. David squatted on the pallet behind him trying to quiet him.

"I must have been dreaming," Mu San mumbled, still

held by the anguish of his dream—he a student only recently arrived in Peking, belonging to the party of neither
the right nor the left, a proud in-between man, respect-
ing the ancient belief in compromise. He had been asleep
in the dormitory the night that Chiang Kai-shek's secret
police gained entrance and dragged him away with other
students, accusing them of being Communist—the torture,
the horror, screams of girls who had been taken to another room to be questioned had entered his dreams. Fu Fu,
as they called her, beautiful Fu Fu of the delicate hands.
His return and hers. The nailless fingers of her right hand
forever a reminder of the night's ordeal. He would have
nothing to do with what Chiang offered, but would take
the Communist way. Violence, extremes, seemed to lie in
both directions.

"It is nothing," he said. "A bad dream. I'm not a good
sailor." But for a moment more he leaned against David.
With the young body sagging against him, the older man
felt emotion rising in him. So might he have felt toward a
son who was in trouble.

Chapter 9

DAVID FLUNG WIDE THE
cabin door and the sunshine poured in. The junk was sailing on a comparatively smooth sea. Men and women were emerging from their cabins, calling, gesticulating over the violence of the storm and the havoc it had wrought—"Ai yah, Ai yah," they exclaimed. The foresail had been split off near the base and had disappeared in the sea. The mainsail, upon examination, was badly torn. Immediately sailors were set to work mending it—a brown patch, next a red one. The laodah had already been released from the rudderpost; a sailor had taken his place.

Young Chen's servant went about preparing warm

144

foods. While they waited Mu San and David drank hot tea which one of the boatwomen brought them. A friendlier spirit seemed now to exist between the two. It was as if in that moment when Mu San had accepted the support so naturally given by the older man some understanding had been achieved which had been denied them before. They were content with a desultory conversation mostly about the possibility that their junk might have been driven far off its course, but neither seemed to have the energy to seek out the answer from the boat people. The relief from the violence of the storm was enough just now.

David, revived by the tea, and unable to forget his boyhood friend, Lo, asked, "By any chance, when you were at the university in Peking, did you know a professor by the name of Lo Sun San? I believe he was still teaching there as late as 1948. He was a boyhood friend of mine. I hope nothing has happened to him."

"There was such a professor, I believe. I had no classes with him," Mu San answered casually. He looked out to sea lest he show in his face the emotion the name Lo Sun San had aroused in him. Lo was the revered teacher who had shown him the values of communism, now a prominent official in the Shanghai government.

"It's a pity you had no work with him," David went on, "he must have been a wonderful teacher. I can still remember his beautiful voice. He planned to teach literature. The year after I left China, for my college education in America, he lived with my father. He was really a son to him. I'm sorry I've lost track of him. He might help us now."

David found himself telling the younger man of the close relationship between his father and Lo the winter of 1919. "Bertrand Russell and John Dewey lectured in Peking that winter. They often came to see my father and Lo had a chance to know them personally. Lo's letters to me were full, especially, of Dewey's teachings—the idea of not breaking completely with tradition seemed to take a powerful hold on Lo. I hope nothing has happened to him."

"Not that I know of," Mu San answered. "If you will excuse me I will find out how near we are to our destination." This talk about Lo filled young Chen with elation. Everything was clear to him now—this innocent would be the prize he would deliver to his honored teacher, Lo, when they reached Shanghai. Where had the American been, all these years, that he didn't know that Lo was a prominent Communist?

The boatmen were vague in their answers. The laodah was asleep, they could not wake him to ask him such a question. How could anyone know the distance? If the spirits gave a following wind, it was short; if a head wind, the distance would be long.

Night came and with it a sudden change in the junk's course. The laodah again took the steering gear into his expert hands, ordered the auxiliary engine shut off. Silently, slowly, under a light wind they moved toward the land. Quietly the anchor was lowered.

"Are we to get off here?" Mu San asked the laodah.

"Not here. Soon."

A sampan came alongside and the laodah went down the junk's side and dropped with a soft thud into it. There was a swish of waters parted by the oar at the stern as the sampan moved off in the darkness. A long wait before the captain returned. Then the junk moved out of the cove. Had some word been sent ahead to explain that they had been delayed by the storm?

All the next day there was an atmosphere of tension on the junk. The boat people seemed alert to some approaching crisis. David and Mu San were silent; the understanding between them seemed hourly to grow less. Friendship was a silly bourgeois conception, Mu San was thinking. He kept planning how he would deliver the hated foreigner into the hands of Lo—Lo, supposedly the man's friend. What a joke! According to the old saying of his fathers, Mu San laughed in his sleeve thinking how silly the foreigner would look when he stood before Lo. As the day progressed David found that some time during those many hours given over to his memories his decision had been made; he could not abandon Damon. Neither of his parents would have allowed him to do so cowardly a thing. It was too late for detachment.

Toward evening the laodah informed them that sometime during the night they were to leave the junk. Then Mu San prepared David, helped him dye his hair black, darken his skin.

About midnight the auxiliary engine was shut off. Under a following wind they moved forward, finally anchored. Still David and Mu San waited for their orders.

Finally a figure, no more than a darker shadow, rose above the side of the junk. Seeing Mu San, he cried out, "Son of my benefactor!"

"You—" Mu San faltered.

"I am among those rescued by your father's good offices."

"Landowner Wu!" In a time of famine he had once refused rice to the starving peasants until they surrendered to him the deeds to their rice plots. Mu San felt indignation against his father who would save such a one.

"The man who brought him here will take the young master and the foreign one to the shore. Climb to the top of the sea wall and wait until you see three tiny flashes of a light," the laodah instructed them.

Without luggage, a few necessities tucked into the waistbands of their trousers, without clothing other than that which they had on, they lowered themselves into the sampan alongside the junk.

Chapter 10

CROUCHING LOW IN THE SAMpan, David and Mu San could dimly discern a figure at the stern manipulating the oar—a moving blackness in the black night. The faint friction of wood upon wood as the oar revolved in its socket and the falling away of water pushed from the prow as the small craft was sculled forward were the only sounds. A slight jolt told the two men that the sampan had touched land. Stepping off onto the muddy shore from which the tide had recently retreated, they felt their way up the broken sea wall. At the top they stood waiting. To each the breathing of the other seemed too loud.

A tiny light seeming no larger than a firefly flashed once, twice, three times—their signal. Relief spread through David; Mu San let out his breath. A voice whispered, "I will guide you along the dykes by a rope I now place in your hands. One pull, the way is toward the right, two pulls, toward the left." A hand arranged them one behind the other. A light rope held by their guide was slipped to David's hand and Mu San held the end. Quietly they got under way.

In the night the dykes, built a couple of feet above the rice paddies, were precarious, narrow thoroughfares. When they strayed a few inches to either side rough grass warned them that they were near the edge of the embankment. If one should step over the embankment he would pull the others with him down into the paddy below. Gradually a rhythm of movement was established between them—to the right, to the left, they moved deeper and deeper into the country. Soon the smell of the sea was gone. The black earth of the little fields, fertilized for centuries, gave off a peculiarly familiar odor. Now the guide, pulling his followers with him, mounted the steps of a bridge, descended the steps on the other side.

The dank smell of the sluggish waters of the canal assailed David's nostrils as had the earth odors from the paddy fields. Again they trod the dyke paths. The rice heads, ripening now in October, stirred by a night wind, made a soft, grating sound as they rubbed together, smells, sounds come out of the past. At last David walked again upon this earth where he had been born, where his parents had died. This land was his home, the womb from which he had come. But this stealthy travel in the night—a sob rose in his throat.

Mu San was stirred also by this return to the land of his ancestors. For centuries they had been buried in its soil. The abode of his ancestors lay cupped in the hills far away in the province of Shensi. There he must go to find Third Uncle who had been left to tend the low grass-covered mound which sheltered the dead and allowed them to communicate with heaven and earth. Cypress trees rose above the altar standing before the mound. Each year, in the past, Mu San had gone with the men of his family to sweep the graves, bring rice and wine. But his revered grandfather did not lie in the place reserved for him, exiled in death as in life. Mu San felt sudden resentment against this New China which took no count of the dead. Then anger over the bad landlord his father has rescued mingled with his anger over what foreigners had done to his country and he felt justified in the act he intended to commit.

A flock of geese flew over, heralding the dawn.

In the bamboo grove where their guide hid them for the day, they took turns sleeping. One must always be on watch although the chances of being discovered at this time of the year were slight, for there were no bamboo shoots to gather for eating, as in the spring, and no one had time, during the harvest season, to cut the bamboo poles for household uses. Such work would come later. But if both slept and one snored, a peasant passing to his field might hear it and hunt them out in their hiding place. Once discovered, they would be taken to the authorities, the guide had told them. David's presence in the country would mean they would both be executed as spies. Punishment was swift in the New China.

David took the morning watch and when the day drew on toward noon and the sun filtered straight down between the green boles of the bamboo Mu San took his place. The American slept heavily, tired out with the night's march and the morning vigil. An hour passed, two: young Chen, son of a rich man, reared in ease and comfort, had eaten nothing since leaving the junk except some cold rice smelling of the oil paper in which it had been wrapped; he had had nothing to drink except half-warm tea which their guide had left them. Mosquitoes tormented him despite the citronella spread on his hands and face. He had been cautioned not to smoke even one cigarette.

Each passing hour his discomforts bore down upon him more heavily. Already he could feel the hand of the State crushing him down into its disciplined groove even as the peasants around him were disciplined. He, too, in the new State would have to work. These peasants owned their own fields, so the State said, but they did not nap comfortably in the heat of the day as peasants always had. Would he, too, have to give account of each hour? Without break, from the paddies surrounding the grove, came the soft thud, thud of bundles of rice stalks beaten against the sides of the bins to loosen the rice heads.

His enthusiasm for the new State began to ebb. He heard singing. Raising himself cautiously, he saw a group of Yang-ko dancers passing along a nearby footpath. Their singing reached him—the old song of the spring planting but changed to glorify the plentiful harvest brought by the State, the bringer of all good. In Peking, in welcome to Father Mao, Mu San had rejoiced that the traditional song of the Yang-ko had been changed to fit the purposes of the New China. Now he was alarmed. Would the heritage of learning, some of the writings dating back thousands of years, so carefully guarded by the Chinese scholars also be changed to glorify the New China?—Mu San's life was grounded in this accumulation of Chinese scholarship. To have it changed was to lose it; to lose it was to lose himself. Yet he understood the Communists meant to rewrite Chinese history to conform to Marxist doctrines.

Then, like a shaft of light, assurance shone down upon him. The treasures of learning were safe from destruction. Copies of the ancient writings were preserved in America, England, France and Germany. On his travels he had seen such collections. He remembered vividly the day he had spent in the Congressional Library in Washington. He remembered the American scholar who had led him through the stacks, he who through years of effort had patiently collected these Chinese writings. Together they had looked reverently at one classic after another, discussed Lao-tse, Confucius, Tu Fu, the Ping Ming Mei—poets, historians, novelists.

That day he had not hated America. Why did he now? The wavering pendulum of his emotions swung over from hate of America to gratitude. Needless this swing from one anguish to another. After this mission was completed and the two Americans were brought safely out of China, why not go back to that great library in America and there pursue the cloistered life of the scholar for which he was fitted? There he would find sanctuary, join the ever-growing group of Chinese scholars living abroad, follow a life of study and contemplation—be again the superior man.

The sun's rays fell slantingly between the pole-like trees. David woke. A pale-green twilight descended upon them. The last peasant was leaving the nearby fields. They saw him stoop, pick up a handful of dirt, rub it between his fingers, then return it to the field. Both men had heard tales of peasants getting up in the night to go out to their fields to hold a bit of dirt in their hands. Only thus, according to the Communists, did the deeds to the land seem real to these peasants, landless for centuries. Was this peasant so engaged or was he testing the quality of the soil? David thought the latter—probably; Mu San was impressed.

Now that the peasants had left their fields, there was silence except for the croak of frogs. The two men whispered together. It grew late. Both were chilled by the night mist. At last they saw firefly flashes among the trees, the sign that someone of the underground had come for them. The voice that now whispered instruction to them was not last night's voice, but a new one.

Skirting the towns lest someone hear them and give warning that the strict curfew law was being broken, they repeated the intricate pattern of the previous night's march, this way, that way, along the dyke paths. After two hours they came to a farmhouse set in the midst of bamboos. The guide led them through an opening in the bush fence, then through a low doorway. After the door was softly closed behind them, a candle stub was lighted and set in

the midst of its own grease on a table. From the darkness
beyond a woman's brown hand reached out and placed
upon the tables two bowls. One held steaming hot rice,
the other hot vegetables. A pot of tea was added. The two
ate and drank, then gratefully they seized the hot, wet
towels offered them and passed them time after time over
their faces and hands. How did it come, David asked himself, that peasants were a part of the underground? Mao
Tse-tung had made the peasants the foundation of his
revolution.

For six nights they followed guides—ghosts whose faces
were never seen, whose voices were only a whisper. The
nights of travel varied little, but their hiding places during
the day did: the bamboo grove the first night, a farmhouse
the second, the ruins of a landlord's compound the third.
By evaluating every gesture, every chance word spoken,
each pieced together the China in which he must now perform the mission he had undertaken—a faceless land, filled
for each with ghostly voices echoing in a vacuum-created
fear: how to bring a daft man to safety filled David with
anxiety; impossible, Mu San concluded, to rescue the
member of the Chen family hunted by the New China.

Two days and a night they spent under the floor boards
of a cargo boat on a populous canal. It was then that they
touched the violent quick of the revolution. The boat,
meant to be their hiding place for only one day, was one
of many tied up in the crowded canal fronting a market
town. Evidently one of the open-air theaters so common
to China was not far from the canal, for the two men could
hear plainly the high-pitched voices of the actors. Immedi-

ately, Mu San recognized that *The White-Haired Woman* was being played, the play which had been sweeping over all China and which Mao Tse-tung was supposed to have written.

The high keening voice of a slave girl was heard, lamenting how she, the daughter of a peasant, had been forced into service in the landlord's house, tortured by the landlord's wife, raped by the landlord's son. Pregnant, threatened with death, she had escaped over the wall. Pursued by the landlord's agent she had fled, no one knew where. Only her shoe was found by the river's edge. Her wild songs of despair reached the two men—"In my grief, my degradation I hide my face behind my long white hair."

Now came scenes of the revolution when the landlord, fearful of retribution, went to the temple to pray for mercy. A woman with long white hair appeared. He thought her the Goddess of Mercy. She, the girl he had wronged, trembled before him, but the army of liberation offered her protection and the landlord, the wife, the son, the agent, were presented to the audience for justice. Over the girl's song of hope, vibrant and electrifying, the audience, its anger roused to white heat, demanded the life of the landlord, any landlord! All landlords! The terrible words "da, da, kill, kill" reached the two men hidden under the floor boards of the cargo boat.

Mu San lay rigid, ensnared in symbolism. Up from the dark and troubled depths of his people's suffering rose emotions engendered by subjection, years when long hair meant subservience to outside rulers, the Manchus who inflicted the queue which made a man into the guise of a woman. Deeply buried humiliation, other subjections—humiliations from Western countries.

David felt the very air charged with violence, a violence which came close, closer when the audience, aflame now, raced across the boats, hunting out men cowering in corners—landlords, merchants, anyone who was not a peasant. The two under the floor boards scarcely breathed, knowing their danger if they were discovered; only the thin boards protected them from the maddened men. Suppose the boatmen should give them to the mob filled with the lust for blood?

Into Mu San's very soul reached the men's cries of kill, kill. He, too, would kill. With difficulty he kept his hands off the throat of the foreigner who lay so near him. Wait, wait, deliver him to public condemnation when they reached Shanghai. Lead him into a trap, baiting him with his friendship with Lo.

The night was filled with shouts and cries. Finally the night was still. The boatman whispered, "The countryside is not safe. They hunt out the landlords." Only two nights later did the frenzy subside. Then and only then were they released from their cramped confines.

At last came a night when each sensed that they were nearing Shanghai. They had been walking several hours when they saw a faint glow in the sky, undoubtedly the reflection of the lights of Shanghai. There were larger towns strung along larger canals. In place of the steps which lead up and down the bridges over the canals were ramps better fitted to ricksha traffic. Their guide at first skirted the villages, keeping to the country, but finally there was no countryside left, instead continuous villages, one merging into another.

Suddenly the glow died from the sky like a great lamp blown out. Curfew, thought David, curfew when any man going abroad was suspect. Would they hide for the rest of the night? The answer came when the guide led them from the flagged path on which they had been walking down an embankment into a bamboo grove, and whispered, "The honorable two must separate here. A man will take the honorable foreigner to the hiding place in the city; the honorable Chen will come later." Into David's hand was slipped a soft felt hat. Knowing it was given him to hide his foreign features, he pulled it down well over his eyes. "Lai, come," said a new voice, and David, first touching Mu San's hand in mute farewell, allowed himself to be led out of the grove.

An hour of fast walking, then he and his guide entered the outskirts of the city with its narrow congested streets. Hugging the heavy shadows under the eaves of the shops, stealthily they moved forward. Once a chuckle broke from the guide. Fool! Only a crazy man would take any chance when engaged in so desperate an undertaking. The perspiration rolled down from under David's hat into his eyes. But nothing happened even though to David the man's chuckle seemed to resound in the empty street.

Finally his guide knocked softly on the shutters of a shop. Cautiously one board was slid away. Automatically lifting his feet over the high doorsill, a lesson learned in childhood, David followed his guide into the shop. The shutter was slid quietly into place. Shading a flashlight with his hand, thus throwing the light downward away from his face, the man who had let them in led them through the front shop to an inner room. "We are safe here," he said, and he lighted a small lamp.

For the first time David saw the face of his guide, and it was a familiar face, none other than that of the jockey, Han Te Lin, who had ridden David's ponies in the old Shanghai days when he had had his own stable, Te Lin, a ne'er-do-well who gambled away all his earnings but who was a wizard with ponies.

"You!" David gasped.

"In the past the honorable master saved my humble self from prison. Now that prison yawns for him I repay the debt. They asked for volunteers from the underground for the difficult task of smuggling a foreigner into the city." Again the chuckle. David marvelled and took heart. In this gambler there existed the ancient code of friendship! The small kindness of saving the gambler from a debtor's prison was being repaid a hundredfold. Then David smiled, knowing Te Lin. Combined with the duty of saving a friend and benefactor undoubtedly was the man's delight in the game of chance. The underground was the great gamble. He couldn't resist the chance to bet even on his own life!

After so many moments of anguished doubt experienced since leaving Hong Kong as to whether he was in the hands of friend or foe, David felt an upsurge of renewed faith. Had he not come safely to Shanghai under the friendly aid of an underground evidently well organized and responsible. A Chinese had again demonstrated that responsibility to a friend still motivated the Chinese people. The idea of rescuing Paul Damon did not seem as impossible as it often had on the journey.

The shopkeeper brought in food and drink. "Rice is high, too high. Everything is taken for the soldiers. I must buy the cheapest food or the tax commissar will levy another tax on me, thinking I have money hidden away. I cannot stand another tax."

They washed the coarse millet down with the tea, not the good tea of China made from the young buds but that made from the coarse leaves and twigs, evidence of the shopkeeper's genuine poverty, not poverty assumed to be polite in the eyes of his guests.

Shanghai was beginning its day's work. They could hear the shutters being taken down from shop fronts along the street. "Hi ho, hi ho," came the cry of a carrier of night soil as he passed down the street to deliver his load to the fields beyond the city. These were normal Chinese sounds that gave David the sense of a normal world and he began plying Te Lin with questions. "Are many foreigners left in the city?" he asked.

"British firms."

"But no Americans?"

"A few."

"And the head of the bank? Mr. Damon?"

"I know not. At the French Club the British gather— sometimes. They're prisoners though. They cannot go outside Shanghai. They cannot go to their own country. Ha, the new government! Te Lin defies them." He snapped his fingers. "Open up," he commanded the shopkeeper. "The girl will be arriving with the other one. This is the hour for her arrival. She must come boldly in through the front shop with the honorable Chen's son."

David smiled, if a little nervously, at the strutting, posturing Te Lin. The new regime could never be repressive enough to stifle the love of the dramatic in the Chinese, he reflected as he sat waiting for Mu San.

"They should be here by now," said the shopkeeper, coming back after opening the shutters.

"Oh, they'll be here soon. You worry too much," said the little jockey. Picking up the teapot he took a long draft from its spout. "Go back into your shop. Act like a shopkeeper," he commanded, putting down the teapot.

Chapter 11

AFTER DAVID LEFT THE BAM-
boo grove, Mu San was prepared for his journey. A man's
voice out of the darkness spoke. "A woman will escort the
honorable Chen. She will take you to the edge of the
city under the garment of darkness. When curfew ends
and day comes you two will walk openly as husband and
wife. If you are accosted you will say your wife is sick
and you are taking her to the health center. See that the
top button of your coat is buttoned. That is the style at
present decreed by the government. It is important that
in every detail you should be correct in the eyes of the
police. Wait for the girl here. I leave you now. She carries

identification papers which you may be asked for by the police." So saying, the man disappeared.

Alone in the grove Mu San waited, taut, nervous. An all but uncontrollable impulse to run took hold of him. He must not give way to weakness. A little longer now and he could join the great new movement. The foreigner was the prize he would bring with him. He would devise some way to get the man to go with him to see Lo. He must wait and plan. He must wait calmly for his guide who would take him to the underground hideout.

Someone touched him on the shoulder and spoke softly. It was the voice of a high-class woman—and young, he judged. A woman's hand was slipped into his. He felt the nailless fingers! Fu Fu! Panic rose in a wave, swallowing him. He forgot there might be others who had been tortured as Fu Fu had been! He was betrayed! Fu Fu! She knew he had joined the Communists after that terrible night; she had berated him for it. "Cowardness," she had called it. He would be killed by the underground who had learned from her that he was a Communist! What could he do, run? No, he had no papers and it was getting light. Make her give him the papers here? No. There might be other members of the underground still in the grove. Go with her, make his escape on the road when he was certain no one was near.

Out on the flagged path his love for Fu Fu overcame him, he could not bring himself to attack her. They walked on silently, she leading, he following. Dawn was just lighting the sky as they reached the first narrow streets harboring the city's poor. Now! He could not wait longer.

With a sudden move he pinned her to the wall, tried to reach in her jacket. "Give me the papers," he whispered. They fought silently. She flung him back against the shutters of the unopened shop. In that moment he saw her face. She was not Fu Fu! He reached for her. He'd kill her! But again she flung him back and disappeared down a dark alleyway, and the identification papers, forged though they were, disappeared with her. He was panic-stricken—no man could long remain free in this city, unidentified. Then relief surged through him. He had a friend in this city. All he had to do was to get to his teacher and friend, Lo, who would identify him. The problem was to avoid policemen as he made his way to his friend's house.

Back in the shop they waited for Mu San and the girl. Even Te Lin was losing his aplomb. Then the shopkeeper came in pulling the girl after him. "Now what do you think, Te Lin? Where is the man?" He hissed out the words.

"Why did you leave it to me to bring this traitor in? Why did you not escort him, little jockey?" demanded the girl, brushing off the shopkeeper's hand. "I was not strong enough to kill him nor to keep him from escaping, but he did not get the papers. He is a traitor to our cause, taking this way of learning about the underground of which his father is a member."

Te Lin spat. "He fouls the nest of his ancestors."

"We'll all have to get out of here." The girl terrified moved quickly toward the front of the shop.

"Be quiet." Han Te Lin with a quick move blocked her

way. "This traitor, this son of a turtle, could only know about the junk. He doesn't know the places he stayed on the way here. He doesn't know this hiding place. We're safe here, as safe as we've ever been—for today. We need rest and time to plan."

The owner went quickly into the front room to make a show of waiting for customers.

The jockey and the girl conferred.

Then Te Lin addressed David. "I go now. I'll return to-night with arrangements made for your honorable safety," said Te Lin. "And do not let the shopkeeper out of your sight. Do not give him a chance to betray us. No man knows whom he can trust. Where will you go?" Te Lin asked, turning to the girl.

"I can take care of myself," she answered proudly. "It was only for a moment I was frightened. I have friends."

"Shopkeeper," she said in a loud voice as she entered the front shop, "does not the cooperative have cloth for a Lenin jacket?" As she stood for a moment in the doorway between the two rooms she was in the light coming in through the open shop front and it fell full upon her. David saw that she had the narrow, aristocratic face of the upper class when young. Then she too went from his sight. Was she friend or foe? Mu San had proved false.

Now David doubted even Mu San's father. He had only Te Lin to rely upon. Would Te Lin ever return? His life and that of Paul Damon for whom he was responsible lay in the loyalty and judgment of this humble one.

Chapter 12

AFTER THE GIRL HAD DISAP-
peared Mu San stood irresolute in the dark alley, not
knowing what to do. By his own stupidity he had lost the
chance to deliver the foreigner to the authorities, a prize
which would have made up for taking matters into his
own hands and entering the country without permission.
Moreover, he had no identification papers. Without them,
he feared if he were arrested he would be dealt with swiftly
and mercilessly. Before police accosted him he must reach
his friend Lo. But how? Although this was his own city
he was in an unfamiliar part of it. Following one alley
after another, finding no sign to tell him where he was,

he was again in panic. He dared not look behind. He dared not stop and ask directions of men who were beginning to take down the night shutters from their shops. Then as he entered a short street he saw that it led into a wide thoroughfare. On its farther side was a bridge which he recognized—the Garden Bridge across Soochow Creek. He had only to turn left on the wide street, pass the Astor Hotel, once the fashionable gathering place of Westerners, take any street leading away from the creek and he would be in a district known to him. In the past less prosperous foreigners, especially missionaries, had lived here among the Chinese. They wouldn't be living here now, he gloated. In fact, Lo's home, he had learned in Hong Kong, was one of the houses once owned by a foreigner.

He entered the wide thoroughfare, crowded with men and women all dressed as he was in loose trousers and Lenin jackets. Assuming a confidence he did not feel, he walked among them. They were all smiling—Chinese did not smile easily—he did not. People looked at him strangely, even with suspicion. A man nudged him. "You do not rejoice with us in the New China." "Yes, yes," Mu San hastened to say and he smiled realizing the smile was a kind of password here which might serve him for the present in the place of an identification card. But he was ill at ease, for despite the fact that everyone smiled, no one joked with his neighbor. There were no loud guffaws, no easy humor such as he had been accustomed to in the past and no street fights.

At the corner of Broadway and Wangpoo Road, where the traffic was heavy, a policeman was directing the crowd.

He wore a sun helmet, his uniform was clean and good—indeed a New China. A man propelling a pedicab was edging his way into the crowd. "Little brother," the policeman called out, "watch yourself, the eye of the State is upon you." Mu San felt it upon him too and upon the man next to him, a carrying-coolie who with Chinese gusto spat on the pavement. Again came the voice of the policeman, "Little brother, there is a container at the corner. Lift the cover, deposit your spit there."

A group of young girls in short blue skirts, white shirts, red ties, the ends fluttering, came along Broadway singing—

> "We love labor, we are valiant
> Every hardship we have conquered."

The crowd joined in the song—

> "Red flags are flying
> The whole world marches."

Mu San took this opportunity when everyone was swept up into the emotion of patriotism, to leave the singing crowd and cut down an all but empty alley. He marvelled at the cleanliness of the city. Even before the meanest stores men were sweeping the narrow space on which their shops fronted. Carefully they carried the refuse to the corner and deposited it in containers, placed there by the new city management, Mu San supposed. Avoiding any conversation with pedestrian or shopkeeper, trying to act as if he belonged among them, little by little he neared his destination. At last he reached the short dead-end street which led to Lo's house. He had been told he would recog-

168

nize it by its position at the entrance to a wall-enclosed compound owned formerly by American missionaries. No signs of them now; no foreigners anywhere. Shanghai given back to the Chinese. Mu San's heart leaped up within him.

At the distant sound of singing coming from behind him, he turned. A band of boys and girls came into sight singing,

"Eastern skies are lit with sunshine!
The light of our future fills us with joy,
Joy, joy."

As they passed, he saw their faces. Never before—no, not in all the world—had he seen such an expression of high mystical endeavor! His throat went dry, his heart quickened its beat—his countrymen, his China no longer defeated! Why had there ever been any doubt where his heart lay? He walked swiftly now, head up, toward his friend's house—a foreign house of two stories, remodelled evidently to accommodate several families. There were two doors on the first floor, and an outside stairway at one end. A small, high-peaked sentry box stood directly in front of it. As Mu San paused not knowing what to expect, a policeman came out and began walking up and down before the house. To pass him was to risk being asked for an identification card. Better to wait. A slight drizzle had begun to fall. Mu San felt certain after a while the man would slip inside the guardhouse for a sip of tea. When no one was looking, despite Communist discipline, surely the man would relax his vigilance as all sentries of all time had done when it was wet or cold and they needed tea to warm them.

Finally, the man entered the boxlike shelter even as Mu San had foreseen, thus giving him the chance to make a dash for the house. He knocked on the first door he came to, the one at the left. A man opened it a crack. "I came to see Mr. Lo on urgent business." "Not here," said the man hastily, closing the door.

Surely Lo was too important to live on the upper floor, thought Mu San and he moved quickly to the door at the right and knocked. Lo himself opened it but a Lo Mu San scarcely recognized! His jet-black hair had turned white, something almost unknown among the Chinese in the past; it hung thick and white over his ears, giving him somehow the appearance of a monk. His black eyes burned with a zealot's light.

Ever since the day when he had left his teaching position in Peking University and marched south with the troops Lo had been wholly committed to the Communist Party serving it with blind devotion. Gradually he had risen to a place in the inner circle. He was a poet called "a spiritual worker" in the New China. A poet at heart, he had found poetry in this new doctrine, the poetry of a new earth. To the making of this new earth he had bent all his energies—individual man incapable of realizing this goal by himself must be transformed by an environment created by the elite, he now one of the elite.

"I have come, honored teacher, to serve the State," Mu San said and bowed low.

"Not teacher, comrade." Lo spoke sternly. "But we

have not been informed that any students are due today.
Where are your identification papers? When did you pass
over the bridge from the British Crown Colony into Free
China?" He did not step aside so that Mu San could enter.

"I did not come by that route."

"There is no other."

"I can explain everything, revered teacher."

"Comrade," Lo again corrected him.

Looking into his eyes, Mu San realized that a great deal
can happen to a man in two years. The last time they had
been together Lo had still been the scholar, Mu San his
disciple—the teacher-pupil relationship. Lo's eyes now
seemed to bore into his former student's very soul with
cool objectivity. A disciplined officer of the State had replaced friend and teacher! No leniency would be granted
to the former pupil, no glossing over of his illegal entrance
into the country, no holding back on naming the ones
who had been his accomplices. Mu San's ecstatic vision
of a few minutes before when he had seen himself at the
white-hot center of the new belief faded. The cold reality
of his dangerous position gripped him. He was aware now
that he had miscalculated in his evaluation of his place in
Lo's present life. His only hope to save his own, and perhaps
his father's, life was to deliver the hated foreigner, David
Conway, as a substitute. But he did not know where the
foreigner was hidden! He had acted in panic, thus destroying the justification for his secret entrance into the country.

Thinking fast, he said, "Comrade, I bring information
of great importance. Let me enter. Food, tea if you have

it. I've been travelling fast in order to bring valuable information to the State."

Lo stood aside, "Enter. Sit if the capitalistic life you have been living has made you so soft that it is necessary." The room the young Chinese entered was monastic in its barrenness. A native bed stood in one corner, a thin pad on its rope springs. A deal table was pushed back against the opposite wall; piles of books and papers were neatly stacked upon it, a telephone occupied one corner. A cheap bamboo stool stood in front of the table.

"Whose permission did you get to enter China?" Lo asked.

"Does a man not know sometimes how best he can serve?" Mu San ventured, continuing to stand, tradition forbidding him to sit as long as his teacher stood.

"You are talking as if you did not know the discipline." There was an expression of distaste on Lo's face.

"Such discipline should be only for children, not for men, and I am a man," young Chen answered angrily, forgetting himself.

"You talk like a counterrevolutionist. I cannot harbor such a one as you." Lo moved toward the telephone.

Young Chen's anger ebbed from him. He was aghast at what he had said. "Honored teacher, let us not quarrel," he begged. "I have dreamed of this meeting for so long."

"Dreamed." Lo seemed aghast at the word. "We are scientists without dreams, working for material advancement. We stand upon the ground of revolution, total commitment to the State in thought and act."

"Let me explain why I have come unannounced," Mu

San pleaded. "I have important news. When I have explained, if you feel I have erred, let me repent and make retribution. I have been held in the capitalist world a long time." Young Chen swayed, exhausted by fear and the rigorous travel to which he was unaccustomed. Lo motioned to the stool by the table. In the distance Mu San could hear a food vendor's bell. His story seemed to slip from him, his mouth watered for the hot sweet potatoes which in childhood he had bought from such vendors. If he could only have something to eat.

"If I *feel* you have erred," said Lo. "I already *know* you have erred. Every word you have uttered indicates your thoughts are wrong. I do not judge your actions. The truth, the body of Communist thought absolute and unchangeable, judges you. I will listen to but one statement. Why did you make this unauthorized entrance into the country?"

"I had the chance to run down an underground movement starting from Hong Kong. I thought the leaders here would not wish me to lose the opportunity."

Even as he spoke Mu San realized that each statement he made mired him deeper in error, but he plunged on. "I had no opportunity to get the consent of the Party. The junk was leaving. I had only time to get on it. I can tell you of the trip and the general position of the cove where we landed. I can estimate the distance from there to Shanghai."

"When did you reach Shanghai?"

"Last evening."

"The hideout?"

173

"En route I came to suspect that they had guessed I was a Communist, loyal to the State. Once we got to their hiding place I felt certain they would never let me go. I broke away as we entered the city knowing my information could be sufficient for the State's efficient police to round up the members of the underground operating from Hong Kong."

Lo looked at Mu San pityingly. "What kind of a revolutionist are you, Chen? A revolutionist who is afraid to risk his life for the cause knows nothing of total commitment. Too, you are obviously not telling us all you know. Now give me *all* the information you have. From where in Hong Kong does this underground operate? This you must know even if you don't know where it ends. How did you come to meet the junkman? Whose tool is he? Whom in Hong Kong are you protecting?" Again Lo moved toward the telephone.

"I will tell you all," cried Mu San. "An American hired the junk to bring him back into China. He used to know my grandfather. He asked me to come with him to spy. He used to live here, knows the ropes. I think you knew him once. At least he said you did—David Conway."

It could not be true that David Conway had returned, thought Lo, the one man from the outside world who could harm him! In his confession made before he could be accepted into the hard core of the Party, Lo had named this man and his father as the associates who had corrupted him. For years now he had thought of them as his past enemies; now the son was a present danger to him, indeed his enemy. To come before the tribunal now and report

174

that the man whom he had denounced as the one who had once weakened him with bourgeois thinking was in the country and yet not be able to tell where he was would make Lo suspect. Would the inner circle think he was hiding the man? Suspicion was a two-edged sword. He, trained to use it against others, feared now it would be used against him. "Tell me how this Conway looks, the color of his eyes?" There was a note of urgency in his voice, Mu San noted.

"Brown."

"His hair?"

"Just now it is black. I helped him to dye it."

Lo spoke gently now. "After all between us there still exists the teacher-pupil relationship. Let there be confidence between us so that we may serve the State. I know that an American could not execute such a plan without such a Chinese to help him. Neither could an underground operate without influential backing. One does not enter China without elaborate and careful preparation. It is not the old lax China that could easily be hoodwinked. Give me the man's name in confidence so that I may use the information privately and kindly. He is probably a very good man, but misguided. Through him we could learn more of this spy who probably gave a false reason for entering the country."

His honored teacher still recognized their relationship! I can trust him, thought young Chen moistening his dry lips with his tongue; he said, "In confidence I will tell you. My father helped this American. But, honored teacher, my honored father is a captive to my honored grandfather's feudalistic ideas. This American traded upon the feudalistic idea of personal obligation. He asked for help to free his substitute, Paul Damon. I always suspected his real intention was to spy out information for his government. My father's part I have told you in confidence."

Lo stiffened. "Such a crime I cannot withhold from the authorities. The tribunal must know of your family's hideous crime."

"But you said it would be in confidence," Mu San protested.

"There is no such thing as the sacredness of confidence in a case like this. That is a bourgeois idea."

Mu San realized he had been tricked into giving his father away. He swayed on the stool. Lo caught him, pushed a pot of tea in front of him. Mu San lifted it in trembling hands, drank in long draughts from its spout. His teacher, the man who had taught him that communism was beautiful, had done this ugly thing to him—betrayed his confidence. Now he knew his father would not be spared. But surely the Communist State could not reach as far as Hong Kong and destroy his father. And then in the midst of his confusion a small sense of personal triumph swept over him. The girl . . . last night . . . she was not Fu Fu. . . . But in some strange way she seemed to be Fu Fu and he had not betrayed her, and he had not betrayed Third Uncle.

"If your fantastic tale proves true, if we find this Conway you speak of, possibly your life will be spared. In the meantime we will hold you as substitute for the foreigner," said Lo. His hand rested on the receiver but he did not lift it, did not call the Central Committee. Before he asked for a conveyance to take him and this former pupil to the tribunal he must decide how much to tell. He who with singleness of purpose had performed every task heretofore set him by the State now sought some way by which he could hold back part of young Chen's story— offer to spare the young man's father if he would forget what Conway's business was in the country? To lie was no error. Then Lo, the genuine convert to communism, drew back in horror. To lie against the State! To what had he fallen! He lifted the receiver and in a clear voice called the office of the secret police.

For hours Mu San was interrogated, still he provided no more information of Conway's whereabouts than he had given Lo. Once he was taken out and whipped, lightly. Youth was precious in the new State and this youth had technical knowledge the State could use. At the end of the day Mu San was thrown into prison. If his tale proved true and the foreigner was found, he would be allowed to live and to study the doctrine. This decision reached by the committee pleased Lo. He coveted this technically trained former student for future service to the State.

Lo headed a special group that indoctrinated young students and ferreted out disaffection among the older intellectuals. That he was also a member of the secret police was known only to the inner circle. In the beginning the cruelties, for so at first he regarded the methods needed to produce complete subjugation among students and teachers, had been repugnant to him, but gradually he had learned to use fear like a knife and thrust it deep into a man's will until the arteries of the mind were cut and opposition was impossible. Lo felt his fear over his own involvement in this episode giving way to the dark ecstasy he would experience in inflicting upon this independent young man the disciplines by which his mind would be brought into subjection. But first the foreigner must be found.

Armed with the infinitesimal clues Mu San had given, the search for David Conway started. Who had once been a friend of Conway's? Who once had been a friend of Damon's? The dossiers of prominent Chinese in and out of the Party were examined for such connections. The dossiers of British and Germans still left in the city were examined for clues. Whom did Conway know among the foreigners? What Chinese had been in his service? The few Americans who were still in the city were in prison and could not hide Conway, nevertheless they were also questioned. Damon, who had sunk into a vast silence, looked up blankly when questioned. He was made to talk.

Along the arteries of fear and suspicion that veined the city the search pulsed and throbbed. Chinese who had once known Conway as banker and Shanghai resident denounced him loudly, told of others who, they claimed, had been closer to him than they had been. A former houseboy of Conway's, when interviewed, informed on Te Lin. "Not only had Te Lin been a 'running dog' of a foreigner; he had served the man in no useful way. Conway was not only a foreign capitalist, he was also a playboy. Te Lin had served him in this capacity, and Te Lin had gambled, now considered a vice in China."

Te Lin, when summoned, was loud in denunciation of his former employer. Conway had left town without paying him for the months ahead, payment which was demanded by the new government of China. And then Te Lin played his trump card. "I am a glorious father, so designated by the State. I have a son, a patriot who chose to fight for the fatherland. I gave him guidance, urging him to serve the State—I think I know who would be likely to hide this good-for-nothing American! Now that I come to think of it, when the hated American left China without paying me he recommended me to a Britisher at the stables who might give me employment. He was a great friend of the American." Te Lin was pleased with his performance—he had succeeded in removing all suspicion from himself and he had evened up his score with the Britisher who had refused to employ him.

Sitting with his wife at dinner that evening the Britisher knew by some subtle difference in the service his houseboy was rendering him tonight that he was again under suspicion for some indiscretion—was it something done recently or years ago?

"No news?" asked his wife.

"No," he answered, aware that she meant was there any chance they might soon be allowed to go home to England.

There was a knock at the door and both started, for a knock on their door usually meant trouble. They waited. Soon the houseboy dressed in the garb of New China ushered in the much-feared police. They were very polite—no one in the New China was rude; to be rude was to lose face. "We are sorry to interrupt your dinner, but we have urgent business." They bowed. "If you will be so good as to come with us. There are questions we believe you can answer." In polite, low voices they forced the man toward the door. No time, no opportunity to assure his wife. But what assurance was there that he would return to her?

In the days which followed, as one blackmailed another, many were caught in the coils of suspicion, questioned, returned to their homes, as was the Britisher, again picked up for questioning, again returned. Some not returned. And yet the American was not found.

Chapter 13

DAVID IN THE BACK ROOM OF the shop, as he waited for Te Lin's return, tried to bolster his wavering confidence in Chinese friendship by going over in his mind the many occasions during the years when he had relied upon such friendship and it had not failed him. Night came and David, not daring to sleep for fear the shopkeeper might flee under cover of darkness and give him away, counted the hours, hoping against hope that the jockey would return. Finally, toward morning he began to lose faith in the man's promises. Why should he return and risk his own life? Rats leave a sinking ship; are human beings any better? How much did any

181

friendship, any personal relationship mean when survival was at stake? White men had betrayed each other right here in this city when the Japanese had taken over; white men had betrayed each other when the Reds took over, and he, a son of John Conway, had betrayed Paul Damon. How could he expect more of the irresponsible gambler than of himself? But in each crisis which had overtaken the city there were both foreigners and Chinese who had not betrayed their fellowmen. It was upon the rock of their integrity he now attempted to stand.

Day came, the shopkeeper opened the shop. All appeared as usual. At noon the man said, "If you continue to distrust me all is lost. It is necessary that I go to the meeting we all must attend at noon to learn the doctrine. If I am not there today, with the city being searched for you, suspicion will center on me."

Yes, David saw that all would be lost if they did not trust each other, but the hour while the man was away was one of terrible suspense. The shopkeeper returned even as he had promised.

Strengthened by the man's integrity David came to a decision. He would not cower in the back room of the shop, endangering the life of this good man. No. He was here to save Paul Damon. In the morning he would go boldly to the authorities, tell them he had returned as he had promised he would. Surely he could free Paul Damon by his own surrender. He would not think of the retribution that might be meted out to him for entering the country without permission. In the past foreigners went freely in and out of the country. Even yet only on the surface of his mind did he realize the bitter hatred against Americans. Belonging to these people since childhood, he refused to believe he was now rejected.

He slept and when he woke it was dark. A rustling. He held his breath. A low chuckle, then a whisper. "It is the good-for-nothing gambler but masterful rider-of-ponies, Te Lin, who keeps his promises even if a mite late."

So Te Lin had not betrayed him after all!

"The little rat, Mu San, gave the underground away. It caused me a little trouble." Te Lin spat, spoke in disgust. "They picked me up, but I got free. I am a great man. There has been conferred upon me the title of 'glorious father.' Glorious fathers are respected in the New China; I have a son who chose to fight the hated Americans in Korea. Behold a glorious father." In the dim rays of Te Lin's flashlight David saw how the man puffed out his cheeks in mockery. For a moment delight in the performance eased him of tension.

"You are a good man," said David. "But it is too much of a risk you're taking. You must go away. I cannot accept so great a sacrifice. I have decided to give myself up in the morning."

"Since that would harm others, shall we gamble together?" Te Lin spoke coaxingly. "Gamble for your safe return to your own country and that of your substitute?"

"Yes, if that is your desire," answered David, catching the gambler's spirit.

"There's a meeting tonight at the People's Plaza, the former place of proud jockeys and ponies. Would that I could show the former race track to you." He spoke with pride, then with disgust—"Meetings, meetings, my head rings with the sound of oratory. Tonight after the meeting the students and workers go to the arena where the dogs used to be raced."

The shopkeeper sitting by David shuddered. "The place of execution," he murmured.

"Tonight a landowner is to be tried in the arena," said Te Lin. "I think it is being done in order to take attention from the failure of the government to locate Conway, the spy. A great parade is planned, starting at the People's Plaza and ending at the arena. It passes by this corner. When it reaches the end of this street we will be there. We will slip into the parade, shout with the others."

"Are you crazy?" protested David.

"You prefer to die than gamble for your life?" The jockey's voice was edged with contempt.

"Go on, tell me your plan in full," said David.

"Shout, sing. Keep your head down."

"Then what?"

"When I touch your elbow, you fall out."

David, his hat pulled low over his eyes, walked quietly behind the jockey, stopped when the jockey stopped, moved forward when the jockey moved forward. As they reached the corner there was a sudden burst of sound— beating drums, clanging cymbals, chanting voices. As the parade came abreast of the two, Te Lin waited, only stepping from the side of the road into the marching throng when the stragglers were passing. David slipped in behind him. All around him, above him, banners bearing the slogans of the Party dipped and swayed, drums beat, cymbals clanged, voices chanted, "We advocate the five loves—love the fatherland, love science, love the people— the right people, those who accept the doctrine. Kill all Americans who kill our brothers in Korea." Clang, clang of cymbals. David was borne along by the shouting, singing crowd, he too shouting the slogans.

Slower the movement. Now those around them pivoted upon one spot, waiting for the bottleneck ahead of them to clear. Then the massed crowd suddenly spilled out into an open space. In front was a high platform. To the right and left hung mammoth signs reading "This is the People's ground, redeemed from the hated playboys of the West. Here they raced their dogs." Directly above the platform hung two huge pictures: Stalin and Mao Tse-tung—Mao Tse-tung, the student remembered by David, shabbily dressed, the revolutionary, who in bitterness had eked out a precarious living by carrying newspapers to more fortunate students. The face of Mao Tse-tung, enlarged many times in the picture, was no longer thin, but plump with good living; his black hair, like a child's bob, hung over his ears; his black eyes were inscrutable. The two faces— Russian and Chinese—floated above the black-haired throng, their heads bobbing like black corks amongst the banners and torches; at rest now, the black corks.

There was sudden silence and out of it, over the loud-speaker, came a voice saying, "I wish to make a confession. I have given way to feudalistic thinking. I am guilty of the sin of choosing the means by which an underground plot was to be disclosed. Worse, I held back the knowledge of my father's part in the plot."

It was Mu San's voice magnified by the loud-speaker to reach the vast multitude. Mu San was betraying his father! What then could David expect? He held his breath, waited for denunciation of himself. It did not come. At last he understood: to speak of an American come into the country without permission and as yet at large was to say, in effect, that the State was weak. He was to be hunted secretly. Only when found would he be exposed to public ridicule—humiliation—death.

Despite the walnut juice staining his face and neck, he felt his white body must show through his clothes. He lowered his head to hide his Western features. Lower, lower.

Again Mu San's voice: "I, who should have placed loyalty to the State above wicked subservience to my father, should die for my sin against the State. But let me live to serve."

His voice was drowned now in the voice of the crowd shouting "Traitor." Hundreds of dark-brown hands reached up to grasp the slender, delicate figure on the stand. They reached higher. Men were raised upon men's shoulders. Hands reached closer, closer around Mu San. Suddenly over him loomed another figure shouting into the loud-speaker. "I speak for the jury. Spare this contrite man—young, able to serve the State. We present, in his place, a landowner, an evil man who has made money out of the farmers. His heart is black as a tiger's. We, a jury of the people, have condemned him."

A man clad in the long robe of the upper class, his hands tied behind his back, was pushed forward, forced to his knees. The strong brown hands of workers reached up, up. This time they clasped their prey. David felt a touch on his arm and heard Te Lin shout into the ear of the man near him. "I am a glorious father. My son is a hero in Korea. I have business elsewhere." The thin edge at the back of the crowd gave way before this man honored by the State. David followed close behind.

Soon the two men were in the open. "No need to hurry now. You would like to see the race course?" Te Lin asked.

"If you wish," David murmured, but he feared his savior was overplaying his hand.

When they reached it Te Lin asked with pride, "Is it not beautiful?" Before David was a lake, willows leaned over it. Willows bordered the winding paths; for one instant David was carried back in time. Could it be that China in casting off the West was trying to return to the philosophy of harmony? Then over the loud-speaker he heard the bellow of the mob, "Kill, kill."

They turned into Nanking Road, the once-famed thoroughfare frequented by tourists. "Kill, kill," not so clear now. "No hurry," whispered Te Lin—"two loyal Chinese walking home before curfew." At last he turned into an alley, stopped at a back entrance.

"The bank!" gasped David.

"None other," Te Lin replied. "During the day I run the elevator here. There is an unfinished loft at the top. No one goes there. Hush, the guard comes this way—he has gone now, take my hand." He chuckled. "It is your right to abide here over the heads of the officers of the new government who have stolen this building from you."

Stealthily up the back stairs they went. The top floor reached, a trap door lifted. As they climbed into the loft their feet stirred the dust and David sneezed.

"I have no broom," apologized Te Lin. "But there will be no rats to bother the august one. Our government does not permit rats in the city." Again he spoke with pride. This mingling of pride and derision Te Lin displayed toward the new government confused David, made him uncertain. Then he saw before him the tangible evidence of the jockey's devotion to him. In the light of the flash Te Lin held David saw that this simple man had somehow managed to gather a few comforts for his former employer's use: a Chinese padded quilt, a rice bowl filled with rice, a teapot that was warm to the touch and, of all unessential things, a pack of cards! At least just now, when he wanted nothing so much as water to cleanse his sweaty body, so the cards seemed. Then he was filled with shame. What kind of person am I? he thought. This jockey has risked his life to gather these things for my comfort. "You are a good man," he said for the second time that night.

"Make no noise during the day," cautioned Te Lin. "Stay quiet. Stir not the dust lest the honorable one sneeze. My unworthy self may not be able to get food to you regularly, but trust this unworthy one who must go now. In a few moments the curfew will sound."

Te Lin disappeared in the darkness below as David held the trap door open, then fumbled his way back to the quilt and sank down upon it. His exhausted body cried out,

"Sleep, sleep," but there was no sleep. Instead each tiny nerve in his body throbbed with its own particular memory of the night's happenings: Stalin and Mao Tse-tung, Mao the inscrutable—the once poverty-stricken student looking down on the still-elegant Mu San denouncing his father; the landlord, substitute for Mu San, handed to the crowd; the red cart that waited below the platform for the victim. David's ears rang with the conflicting songs of high endeavor and hate. They sang of the liberated areas, the people's happy places—and they sang—

> "Lift high your mailed fist
> Strike dead the American traitors
> We demand their blood."

It was only a matter of time before they found him; there would be no mercy—he, David Conway, symbol of America, once their friend now considered their enemy, would kneel where the landlord had knelt. No mercy!

David started up. Light! Terror seized him. He had been discovered! Te Lin had given him away! But the loft was empty and very quiet. A pattern half light, half dark, like the pattern of a Venetian blind, lay on the dusty floor in front of him. His gaze moved up the wall to a ventilator; through its slats the sun was shining, making the pattern on the floor.

He rose, folded the thin pad on which he had been lying. Standing tiptoe upon it he could look out between the slats. Below in the autumn sunlight lay the Bund and beyond it the Whangpoo River. In shocked wonderment he studied the scene, a scene changed beyond all recognition. For a century this strip of land along the river had been the pride of the white man; the white man had taken it when it was nothing but a muddy bank and transformed it into a waterfront of which any Western city would be proud. It was Western initiative which had made Shanghai the center of the commercial life of the East—a city of bustle and gayety, a city of money and power lying beside the Whangpoo. Before, the river was always crowded with cargo and passenger steamers, tankers, and freighters flying their house flags under their national flags, and, anchored among them, fleets of Western warships guarding the great possessions of the white man. He, David Conway, for many years had been an influential part of this Western city.

Now the sun sparkled on a river empty of all the ships of the West, and the wide street running along the riverbank, once crowded with motorcars, his own among them, was empty of foreigners and their cars; instead it was filled with Chinese riding in pedicabs. It's a steal, he thought—what right have the Chinese to all this? What right have they to this foreign bank while I, the manager, am hidden away in its loft!

Deep burning anger rose in him. And then he seemed to be standing on a mountaintop, and a disdainful young Chinese standing beside him was saying, "His Satanic majesty offered a Christian man all this in exchange for his soul." And David remembered that behind Shanghai's Western glitter the West had allowed women and children to exist in virtual slavery in the factories, political refugees used its protection while they plotted against the government.

He turned away, spread out his pallet, lay down, sat up, lay down. The empty minutes, the hours began to fill with memories of last night—that split second when his life hung on slipping into the crowd behind Te Lin at the right moment. He must not think about it—nor of the frenzied mob, their hands raised to grasp the landowner offered in young Chen's place, offered in David's place. He saw the worn and dirty pack of cards lying beside the teapot. Quickly he spread them out and dealt himself a hand. Feverishly he played a game of solitaire, another, another. He had himself in hand now.

Up to him from the street below came singing:

"Follow, follow Mao Tse-tung
Follow, follow Mao Tse-tung.
What we demand for the people is
independence.
They cannot be American slaves.
Follow, follow."

Drawn irresistibly to the aperture above him, David again mounted his rolled-up pallet and looked out. A band of young people were marching along the Bund—young pioneers. He remembered seeing bands like this one in the first days after the Reds entered Shanghai. He knew them by their red neck-scarfs, set flying as they marched to the rhythms of their clapping hands. They were singing with gusto.

"Good Chinese boys and girls
Resist America, assist Korea
Defeat the savage-hearted American wolf."

They had passed now. He could no longer hear the staccato clap, clap. Fascinated, he stared at the sight below him! No signs of wealth anywhere; no sleek Chinese women in their long silk gowns slit to the knees getting out of handsome cars; no handsome cars; no elegance anywhere. The variegated pattern of riches and poverty which had always been Shanghai was gone—the silks of the rich, the rags of the beggar. Everywhere men and women were attired in the short Lenin jacket and trousers.

Suddenly it struck him that some physical transformation had taken place in the Chinese. The young people no longer looked fragile or delicate; instead sturdy, vigorous. How had they broken the languid sheath that so long had enclosed them? Again and again during the day he looked through the spaces in the ventilator, fascinated by this new vitality and physical vigor of the Chinese. Gradually he began to feel there was something abnormal in the vitality. It was excessive. Excess in a country whose ancient philosophy was the median way seemed strangely out of proportion.

Memory stirred. Something his father had said on that night so long ago in the Western Hills outside of Peking just before David left for America. "Even if communism takes over, in time I am certain China will steady herself, be tempered by her ancient philosophies. History shows that imported philosophies grow like rank weeds for a time in China—Buddhism, for instance. You see it now subordinated and brought under control by the Confucian philosophy. When it came in from India, it carried men away. Millions left their families to become priests and nuns, breaking the continuity of the family. Men, women and children wrapped themselves in cloths soaked in oil and went singing to their deaths. But after a while the nation returned to the peculiar sanity which characterizes Chinese civilization."

Now he noticed something more in the scene below him which he had not been aware of before. Willows had been planted along both sides of the Bund—old China edging the violence of revolution with harmony. Time will do its work. But time will not serve *me*, he thought, turning away in despair from his peephole. This hate for America was morbidly excessive. All the mistakes the West had made were at present laid on America's shoulders. America who originally had proclaimed the "open door," who alone of all the Western countries had protested when Japan had seized Manchuria. A fragment of song drifted up to him.

"American wolf gives arms to Chiang Kai-shek!"

Two days and nights passed and Te Lin did not return. The tea and rice were gone when on the third night the trap door opened and closed behind the little jockey.

"Your unworthy servant could not come before. Every-where they look for you. They have caught the junkman who brought you to the coast. By torture they have learned all he knows of the underground. His family has been executed."

"Not all the women and children that were on that junk!" exclaimed David.

"If one is guilty all are guilty," Te Lin said, accepting the idea of the solidarity of the family. "Mu San is in prison," he went on. "They do not trust him when he says he does not know where you are. Even glorious father has been watched. Excuse my negligence. Pardon my unworthy gift. My old woman spies upon me." His offering, cleverly suspended inside his Lenin jacket, indeed was small—a bottle of tea, a handful of dried fish and a persimmon. "I know not yet what we can do to save you, but let your heart be at rest, my unworthy self will find a way."

For a long time after his faithful friend had gone, David held the persimmon. He would not eat it just yet. The first persimmon of the season, the signature of the beautiful Chinese autumn of still sunlight, had brought back to him the memory of his old friend Lo. On the last day spent in the Western Hills before leaving for America for his college education, David had stood with his father on the terrace of the temple looking down the path winding through the valley and watched a young man who, as he came nearer, proved to be Lo. After he had greeted them he had placed on the stone railing of the terrace a small bundle, a square piece of cloth, its four corners tied together over the contents. Untying the knot, he displayed the first persimmons of the season, an offering indicating friendship, healing the bitterness of those final days of the term when nationalism had driven out understanding between East and West. Through the palms of his hands David felt the silk-skinned, rounded fruit.

Chapter 14

IMPRISONED AND UNDER SPE-
cial guard, Mu San feared for his life if the foreigner was
not found. Even if he was found, still there must be punishment of some kind. Mu San tried to figure out why he
had been spared, for no sentence as yet had been pro-
nounced upon him. Had Lo intervened for him? The idea
of friendship died slowly in Mu San's mind. All around
him were prisoners who had been committed for less
heinous crimes against the State and they were to be punished with death or hard labor. An old merchant in the
crowded cell whispered, "I hoarded, so they say. I am
to be sent north to help build the new railway. I shall
never again see my family."

The days were spent in enforced penitence and study. Over and over he wrote out his crime against the State, thinking for himself was his crime. He had no right to take it upon himself to pose as a member of the underground in order to learn its secrets. Even if he had planned to deliver the foreign banker he was guilty of individualism, choosing the method by which the spy was to be apprehended. Besides this error of individualism he must cleanse himself of all middle-class loyalties—loyalty to family and friends must be transmuted into loyalty to the State. The ways of his father and father's father must be renounced.

Over and over he read the lessons—"China reconstructs." The masses were changing the face of China. The Yangtse had been swept clear of the ships of capitalistic countries. So had the Whangpoo, which connected the great city of Shanghai with the Yellow Sea and the Yangtse. These were gateways through which the West had brought trade and Christianity to oppress China.

Mao, the great savior, the great father, was developing a rich hinterland deep in the interior of China. A north-south railway far away from the coast beyond the reach of the exploiting West, a railway linking China with the Communist Republic of Mongolia, was being built. China and Russia were again in communication over the old silk route once travelled by Marco Polo. This railroad, when completed, would shorten by a thousand miles the route now used to bring war supplies to Korea from Russia— Russia and China would be a thousand miles closer to each other.

197

A poem learned in his childhood came back to Mu San. He could see his great grandfather, a venerable old man with a thin white goatee, clad in a heavy silk robe, his hands on his knees, reciting in exquisite Mandarin:

"My heart recalls our escape—
We endured dangers, difficulties.

Famished, my foolish girl baby gnawed me.
Little son understood the situation better.

In mud, in mire, we dragged, clung to one another."

And the old man had stopped his recital to explain. "For many centuries it has been in men's minds to guard against the North. Whenever the guard has been relaxed—encroachment. Mongolia taken from China, North Manchuria taken, Russia wanted its timber long ago. Remember what our great and honored poet Tu Fu has written." The old man had gone on with the poem,

"My heart recalls our escape—
We endured dangers—"

Desperately Mu San tried to put aside such bourgeois memories. Desperately he tried to forget the beloved old man who had taught him to fear the great country to the north, to forget his family, but now feverish from the welts, the result of the beating he had received at the hands of the Communists he had come to serve, he longed for his family, for their love, for their understanding, for the ministrations of the good peasant woman who was his mother, for his father's reassuring presence. But he had betrayed them all—outside, outside, desolation, loneliness outside, outside the family!

He went on with his reading. All honor to the patriot who was the creator of this railway. He was a veteran of the long trek over the mountains, across the rivers to Yenan in that epic march of Communist suffering and survival. Made creative by years of hardship, this man is creating much out of nothing—old railway ties, discarded engines, cars, mechanical parts, these things rescued and reshaped, metals ingeniously fashioned to new uses, would complete this railroad leading north. For labor there were the Chinese masses, rich and poor, those whose thoughts could not be reshaped, scholars who would not learn, and the old whom the State could spare.

A fragment of history came back to Mu San; the Great Wall had been built by toiling men and women. Stones built into it were stained with blood not erased by the centuries. History repeating itself? How to kill memory? Man was memory. Memory lurked in every fibre of his being!

His prison companion, the old merchant, mumbled, "Sent to do hard labor, I will die carrying baskets of dirt suspended from a shoulder pole to build the railway embankment."

"Don't talk words, old man," hissed Mu San. "Shut up or I will tell the guard that you complain and they will kill you."

In the ensuing quiet induced by his threat, Mu San pondered on the incredible accomplishments of the New China. A railway line to the border of Indo-China. Once

Indo-China had paid tribute to Peking. She would again be brought into the empire.

A mere woman, an engineer dedicated to the New China was working to control one of China's most devastating rivers. Already she had reservoirs built to contain the flood-waters. No longer would there be periodic floods. Millions of cubic feet of earth had been dug up and carried away to make dams, leaving lakes made by the hands of men. Whose hands? The toiling masses'.

There slipped into young Chen's mind another base thought—ebb and flow, ebb and flow, so had the great Chinese historians seen China's history. After a frenzy of change, after violence and disorder, China always returned to her old ways of serenity and tolerance, so dreamed the scholars of the past.

Then the words Mu San was made to read day after day began to take hold. Man really would be changed. There need be no ebb and flow. The revolution would march steadily forward. The population could double and still there would be plenty, so the books said—eight hundred, ten hundred million people thinking as one, a tremendous power before which the West would tremble, a battering ram to drive against the West.

Mu San trembled with the magnificence of the vision. A hundred years of humiliation at the hands of the West would be wiped out. Now it was the East that would rule the world. Let him only be spared to serve the New China, serve the growing empire!

Chapter 15

THE SLOW DRIZZLING RAINS of autumn came. The damp penetrating cold of winter would soon be here. The little jockey, bound by the old law of gratitude and obligation, schemed and planned to get food to his benefactor, risked his life to get a kettle of hot water from a nearby teahouse into the loft, the only thing his charge ever begged for. But how was he, Te Lin, to get his benefactor out of China? There was no underground to call upon any longer. He had tried to make connections with guerrillas known to him during the Japanese occupation, but without success.

The night was dark, rain was falling relentlessly. It

seemed safe to visit the attic of the bank. Shivering in his thin garments Te Lin started on his precarious undertaking. Under his cotton jacket he held a bowl of mixed vegetables and millet which he had sneaked out of his hut while his wife was gossiping with a neighbor. "No place for a good man now at home," he grumbled. His wife was a shrew. In the old days when he gambled and lost and had no money to bring to her and she complained that he pawned her garments and that he was gambling their livelihood away, he could leave her for a week or two until she was destitute. Then he would return and she would be submissive, but now with this new government she was able to threaten to denounce him.

What was the country coming to with a spy in every house, wives informing on their husbands, children on their parents? Well, if she threatened to accuse him of stealing the bowl of food so he could gamble (forbidden by the State), he'd say he had to give it to the police to protect her against her neighbors who had reported on her gossipy ways. He'd frighten her, tell her how women who could no longer bear children were being taken to work camps, sent north to build railways. Belief in his own abilities to manage his wife revived his spirits. His was a gambler's luck. Something would happen to get the foreign one back to Hong Kong.

The streets were all but empty. Occasionally someone passed huddled under his rain hood or umbrella. Te Lin shivered. The rain and the wind drove through his thin jacket, his cotton trousers clung wet and cold about his bare ankles. He passed the watchman, safely entered the silent building where every footstep echoed, reached the second flight of stairs.

"Don't move, Te Lin."

It was a whisper out of the darkness. He almost dropped his hand from the bowl precariously balanced on his hip.

"Good-for-nothing girl," he whispered back. "I thought you'd deserted. Why'd you have to frighten me? How'd you get in?"

"I followed you, but listen, Te Lin. I have not been able to get to you before. After Mu San gave information about the underground my father's connection with it was discovered. He sent me away to a good peasant, now a guerrilla. My father said one of us must live to carry on the work of the underground. He would not let me die with him." With stoic calm she went on, "We must get the foreigner away tonight. I have information that they suspect you. Let me talk to the foreigner. I can get him away with your help."

"It's three to get out of this building. Too dangerous," argued Te Lin. "Tell me the plan and you leave now."

"No," she said. "Each one has to know his part and learn it. Besides, we've got to get you away too."

So the underground was working, thought Te Lin with relief. Someone with whom to share his burden. Grudgingly he consented to take her with him to the loft.

David, sitting in the dark on his pallet, listening to the drumming of rain on the roof so near his head, was reaching his last reserves. Anything was better than the incessant beat, beat of the rain. Four days since Te Lin had

203

come to him with food. He would give himself up. He would take his chances, make the sacrifice of his life to save Damon's. He would bargain for Paul Damon's life according to good Chinese custom—give his life in exchange for Damon's. But how could he bargain once he had given himself up? Defeat, always defeat. He dozed. In a dream he stood before a tribunal, a tribunal of one person—Mrs. Damon. Her accusing eyes laid bare his guilt. He covered his eyes. He staggered to his feet. "I'll try," he whispered.

Above the rain he heard a noise. Every nerve in his body strained to detect whether it was the rubbing sound of the hinges of the trap door. Yes, the trap door was being lifted. Te Lin? He held his breath, waited. A flashlight so covered as to throw light downward disclosed two pairs of feet moving across the dusty floor advancing, advancing. David held down a scream rising in his throat.

"It is the unworthy one, but not alone," whispered Te Lin. "The girl is with me."

David let out his breath in sudden relief. The two sat down close to him.

Te Lin produced his bowl.

"Eat quickly," the girl commanded. "We must get you out of here tonight." She outlined the plan, began drilling Te Lin in his part, while David ate.

"A tramp is at anchor downstream," she explained, turning at last to David. "If Te Lin can get you there, the captain—a British adventurer who is running the blockade—will hide you, get you back to Hong Kong."

"Tonight!" gasped David. "But I can't go without Paul Damon!"

"He's been executed." The girl made the statement in a flat unemotional tone.

"For what?"

"Many innocent people are dying—especially the innocent," the girl answered.

"When?"

"Recently." Te Lin answered this time.

"Since I reached Shanghai?" demanded David.

"Yes."

So while he had been hiding, Damon's life had been sacrificed undoubtedly in place of his. David had come to make retribution and then had not made it. What kind of man was he—a man without courage or honor. Well, he would show both now. He would not hide longer behind Te Lin bound to him by excessive gratitude and this girl, whose reason for helping him he could not guess. He looked at them sitting cross-legged before him, shivering in their wet clothes—the jockey, his hands clasped within his coat sleeves for warmth, the girl, the tails of her short coat wrapped around her hands.

"I can't let you risk your lives for me. Get out of here as quickly as you can. I've decided to give myself up in the morning." David spoke quietly but firmly.

Impatiently the girl answered. "We've no time to discuss what you will or won't do. Te Lin is in as much danger as you are. His wife has denounced him. She has guessed what he's doing. It's not only you but Te Lin who must get away. We must hurry."

"My wife is the offspring of a turtle. May she remain sterile forever," Te Lin grumbled, getting to his feet.

"I will go," David said, "on the understanding that if anyone stops us, I'll give myself up. You get away if you can. Don't try to save me."

Neither one answered him.

They reached the outer door. Te Lin opened it quietly. No one was in the alley. The girl stepped out and disappeared in the darkness. David drew a deep breath inhaling the fresh air and followed Te Lin out from the shelter of the doorway. They reached the end of the alley; the empty rain-swept Bund lay before them. Was anyone following them? David dared not look, a glance over the shoulder might give them away. He shivered. One block covered; another and another. They were beyond street lamps, darkness was good.

Suddenly light was all around them.

"Stop where you are!" the crisp command rang out.

Te Lin started to run. There was a shot. Had Te Lin escaped? God, let him escape, prayed David, as he was seized from behind.

"You are under arrest," someone said softly. No one in the New China demeaned himself before a foreigner by showing anger. "You are under arrest for spying."

"I did not come to spy—" David began. "I came—"

"You can tell that at your trial. You will please join us in this car." They led him back to the main road where a car awaited them. No crowd gathered. At such a moment people hid in their houses lest they be taken for accomplices.

Up from a deep pit David felt himself slowly rising into some terrible brilliance from which he could not escape; he turned his head but the light followed him. He slipped back into the darkness—rain, the Shanghai Bund, he in clothes thin as a beggar's, he, a foreign banker . . . again the brilliance . . . he was in his own home, the stupid houseboy had turned on all the lights . . . Did he think there was a party?

Slowly David's mind cleared: Te Lin shot and he captured and taken before a group of Chinese to whom Mu San had denounced him as a spy. They had tried to get him to confess that his government had sent him to blow up the waterworks, and the electric plant of Shanghai. Had he confessed to such sabotage? No, of that he was certain. His mind again began to wander. Where was he now? If he could get rid of the light, he could think—where was he?

Slowly, painfully, he brought his mind to focus on his surroundings. He was lying on his back looking straight up into a hundred-watt electric light which was suspended by a long cord from the ceiling directly above him. He sat up and looked around. Why, he was indeed in his own house in the French concession of Shanghai, where all well-to-do foreigners lived—in the fine mansion owned by the bank. The wide windows, black now, for it was night evidently, were framed in the draperies Miriam had chosen. That couch pushed back against the wall—yes, he remembered it. The chairs done in the Chinese brocade which Miriam also had chosen.

A puff of wind sent the heavy fragrance of the que wha across the stale air he was breathing. There was, he remembered, a great tree in the garden covered with the waxen blossoms in the autumn. A sudden memory: he and Miriam were having dinner, they had arrived the night before from America after a leave of absence—he had just been appointed president of the bank; oh, so young his wife looked, doll-like, sitting across from him dressed in some diaphanous white thing; at last he had risen to a position worthy of her; never mind what methods he had used to reach it. They could be forgotten now. Wanting to hold Miriam aloof from the very people who had aided him, he went over and stood behind her chair, put his hands on her shoulders. "My dear, my dear, don't let Shanghai change you." The scene faded; everything in the room was faded, dirty.

Again his mind came back to the present. He was under house arrest until he made his confession; that was what they had told him. The cot on which he was sitting was set squarely in the middle of his own drawing room, directly under the central light.

Without the light, he would be able, he thought, to decide what to do. He rose and walked across the room to the electric switch which he knew was just within the door. "Please do not touch." The soft-voiced command came from somewhere beyond the lighted room. He stood in the broad doorway that led to the hall, also brightly lighted. The door directly across from where he stood, which led into the dining room, was boarded up. The small lavatory at the end of the hall was ablaze with light, its door was nailed open. He understood. He was to have no privacy. He was to live in the glare of continuous light, watched by eyes which he could not see but which could always see him.

Was this what Paul Damon had endured? Was it in this room that his mind had left him? Did he die here, and how had he died? "I am guilty," cried David in his heart. "I sacrificed this man. I should be punished. Oh, Father, nothing they do to me will undo my sin against this man and against you. Let me atone!" Was he praying or calling upon his earthly father—he did not know. One thing only was clear; he must not betray his country, for now he knew which country, in the final analysis, commanded his loyalty.

Out of the darkness came voices, "An American born in China thinks he is a Chinese. An ape strutting like a man." Laughter.

Chapter 16

ON THE NIGHT OF DAVID CON-
way's capture, Mu San had been brought from prison
to confront the foreigner. The fact that denouncing him
as a spy would save his own life was but one facet of young
Chen's exultation. Looking upon this American he felt
cleansed of all bourgeois thinking. All Americans were
guilty of acts of aggression against China, fighting to control Korea was their final outrage. Let David Conway
make retribution.

But on the next day Mu San's exultation was dimmed
when he was again brought from the prison and questioned.
Hour after hour the interrogation went on in an effort to

determine how deeply dyed he was with the middle-class taint of his father. Just why had he taken upon himself to let a traitor enter the country? Why did he not act as a collective man? If he recognized his error, now he would tell them what it was that his father smuggled into the country. Tools—that was in the father's favor and therefore his son's. What cargo did he take out? Opium—to be smuggled into America to destroy Western youth as the West had attempted to destroy China's youth. That too was a good answer although not true.

Were there others besides the two Americans whom his father was trying to get out?

"Yes, Third Uncle."

Did young Chen know where he was hidden?

With dry lips Mu San told where he thought his father's brother could be found.

"He is a landlord?"

"Yes."

"Why did you join in this plot?"

"I wanted to escape my feudalistic father and serve the revolution."

"Why did you search out Comrade Lo?"

"Because he had been known in my student days in Peking as an undercover Communist." Something told Mu San he would be in a better position if he made no claim upon the friendship of his former teacher—this much he had learned since his entrance into China.

The final decision came at the end of the day. Since youth was so precious to the State a chance would be given him to learn to be a collective man. He would be sent to one of the universities given over to full-time thought reform. Here he must stay until his mind was shaped into right thinking.

With a sadistic pleasure never before experienced Lo, as head consultant of student indoctrination, took over the control of his former pupil. To break a mind so proud, so self-reliant could only be done through much suffering on the part of its owner. The suffering of others was becoming a necessity to Lo.

Exercising his power as leader of those who planned the indoctrination of students, Lo pressed the group to which Mu San was assigned to harsher and harsher efforts to divest him of the last remnants of independent thinking. Mu San's mind, trained since childhood to memorize thousands of characters necessary in order to read the Chinese classics, stood him in good stead. Without flaw he soon was able to repeat the maxims of the Party: one, two, three, four, "Every Party member must observe the iron proletarian discipline of the Party. The Party preserves and strengthens its proletarian unity. It purges from its ranks all alien elements and hopelessly incorrigible opportunists." The group made him repeat the last sentence many times, until fear arose in him that they thought him incorrigible.

But he was finding that the maxims he learned one day were often not acceptable the next. He feared his mind lacked the agility to follow the sudden shifts in Communist thought and action. Forward, backward, today not being allowed to think or do what yesterday had been espoused. He found he was loath to acquiesce to an unseen elite which dictated every action and thought. He even asked who it was he obeyed. Was it Moscow or Peking? If it was Peking, was it Mao Tse-tung, or was it Chou En-lai? He was careful not to voice his distrust of Chou En-lai. Mao Tse-tung he regarded as a dedicated man; but he did not believe that Chou En-lai was—he always played with the winning side. This, Mu San knew; in fact, it was Lo who had so informed him in the old days in Peking.

Young Chen tried not to voice his doubt of a member of the inner council but pummeled with questions by this and that member of his group who demanded answers, he grew confused and showed uncertainty. Then followed hours in which the members of his group probed into the very last recesses of his individualistic thinking.

When he heard over the loud-speaker the shouts of the masses, "Kill kill," his body felt cold and numb as it had on the night he had stood before the crowd who had reached for him. Was there evil in such cruelty? By mistake, he had used the word "cruelty" in asking the question. What did it matter that one person was killed? It was not cruelty if it hurried the time of bliss when the united world could shout hozanna, hozanna—the world safe in the arms of communism. Stoic acceptance was the rule of communism; indifference in the face of cruelty, no matter how great the cruelty if it served the larger good. Not for him to decide what was evil and what was good. He must abide by the decision from on high that purges were now needed. San Fan was a drive against corruption among the elite of the Party, therefore no concern of his. Wu Fan, a purge of the capitalists who were left in the country, did concern

him because he had belonged to that class. Surely he wished
to expose any merchant who gave short weight, short
measure, or had two sets of books, one for the State, one
for himself?

He was commissioned, guided by his group, to ferret
out the deception of a merchant who was suspected of
hiding money to avoid buying bonds for the war in Korea.
Young Chen, the son of a capitalist, would know where
merchants hid their money. And indeed he did; members
of his own family, uncles, cousins—taxed by the warlords,
taxed by Chiang Kai-shek—had used various devices to
avoid such taxes, and with a certain amount of safety. Always they were left with enough so that they could start
anew, but the Communists seeking to rid China of the hated
moneyed class did not wish to leave a merchant that
minimum of capital by which he could survive.

When Mu San and his group arrived at the bus station
en route to the merchant's shop, the other passengers made
way for him. Students on a mission for the State were respected, youth was in the ascendancy these days. Also,
there were soldiers accompanying the group. In an un-
natural silence the bus started, the aisles crammed with
those who could not find seats. Mu San felt uneasy with
his oddly subdued countrymen. All his life a public conveyance had been a place for the exchange of insults and
earthy humor.

Down the wide, well-built road, the silent bus careened.
As they swooped around a corner, a fat country woman
fell against Mu San. Hastily she righted herself and offered
her apology to the State. Another curve rounded, and the

old woman pitched backward into the lap of one of the soldiers attached to the group. "The cursed State," angrily shouted the old woman. "Where else can I fall, except into its lap?"

There was a moment of terrified silence. Then the soldier in whose lap the old woman now sat spoke soothingly. "Thus do I serve the people, old Mother." A loud guffaw broke forth from the crowd. Broad jokes, broader retorts flew back and forth. Now that the natural humor of the Chinese had been released, Mu San began to enjoy the ride. Then Mo Tsen, a girl in Mu San's group, spoke admonishing the old woman, and silence again fell on the busload of people. Mu San's happiness evaporated.

They reached the city's edge. Fields of yellow rape and green vegetables dotted the landscape. The winter rain had quickly brought this semitropical, fertile land to a second fruition. The stubbled rice paddies, many of them already ploughed in anticipation of the spring planting, were black patches of earth. Mu San could see peasants walking along the dykes carrying buckets of human excrement to the fields—man replenishing the earth even as the earth replenished him. Through the dark ages and golden so had it been. Inherent in him was a sense of union with the earth. Now looking at the peasants in their blue trousers and short coats he, clad as simply as were they, felt caught up into union with them. "Comrades," he murmured.

The bus jolted to a sudden halt. The driver descended and hunted over the mysterious mechanism for the cause. Lifting the hood, he studied the complicated interior, cursing the mechanism for its stubborn refusal to respond to his coaxing.

Mu San and his group walked along the road where members of a cadre, long trained in Communist methods, stood by a pile of rice bags. "Soon you will see the peasants bringing in their rice," the leader informed the students. "The State is asking an extra quota. The offering needed to fight our enemies is made with joy, as you will see."

Now they heard singing. The sound reaching them was joyous. It echoed over the countryside as the singers came in sight. The peasants drew nearer, baskets of rice swinging from their carrying poles. "Joy, joy." The song grew clearer, stopped as they lowered their baskets before the cadre.

"Is there one among you who has not brought his full offering?" queried the leader. "If so, let him confess his error. Is there one among you who has skimped on his allotment? If I find a shortage when I measure your grain, would you not wish to be held responsible?"

At first no one spoke, for each knew he had skimped a little. But what was a landowner to do? The rice tax was a definite number of catties of rice; sometimes the fields yielded only little more than the tax. Now, months before the next harvest, this extra offering was demanded. How then was a man to feed his family? But the State needed the money for the war in Korea. This was their dilemma: the State had given them the land, each man and each woman a just portion, and they were grateful to the State—but the children, how should they be fed?

"This one." An old man pointed out a stalwart-looking

youth, knowing young men were desired for the army in Korea and knowing also that this man had no children. Then they all cried, "This one! We accuse him of cheating. We deliver him to these kindly officers of the State." Thus they hoped to have their own shortages overlooked.

"Little brother, your neighbors accuse you of wrong. I must deliver you to the police," solemnly said the leader of the cadre.

The rice made the sound of a multitude of tiny pebbles falling upon a multitude of tiny pebbles as it fell into the bins placed to receive the offering—"Ih bai, ehr bai." One hundred, two hundred. With the baskets empty the peasants waited, fearful of punishment. "Little brothers, next time you must do better, but go now." Quickly, except for the stalwart youth, they went back along the path over which they had come. "Joy, joy!" The song grew fainter.

An old man standing by Mu San mumbled, "Joy, we eat bitterness." The old are so stubborn, thought Mu San, trying in his mind to justify the scene he had just witnessed.

The passengers drifted back to the bus where the driver was still struggling with the recalcitrant machine. Another half hour and he shouted, "The bus has given up its evil designs against the State. It had allowed dirt to collect on the carburetor. I have set things to rights. If the honorable group serving the State will take their seats, we will proceed."

"Comrade," gently Mu San reprimanded the driver, "you forget the teachings."

"Comrade," humbly the driver mumbled, "but do not

report me. The new phrases come slowly to the tongues of the old."

As they neared their destination Mu San grew increasingly uneasy. He believed the tracking down of merchant Wang's money was a special assignment designed to test him, to find out whether he could be depended upon to help destroy capitalism. He was fearful that the girl Mo Tsen, a commoner and the head of his group, meant to inform on him if he showed any tendency to favor the merchant. When he had first come among them she had been anxious to help him. But when he did not respond to her amorous advances she had turned to a man of her own class, also a member of the group. Since then in the daily discussions the two often accused Mu San of wrong thinking.

Although it was late in the morning when they reached merchant Wang's shop, the night shutters had not been taken down. "Open to the State," the soldiers commanded. When there was still no sound from within, they banged with the butts of their rifles on the heavy wooden planks. Once! Twice! Three times! Still no answer. This was an insult to the State not to be tolerated. They were about to knock down the shutters when they heard from within a woman's voice urging someone to open the shop, and the querulous voice of an old man arguing against it. Slowly two of the planks were taken out of the sliding groove that held them in place.

Students and soldiers stepped over the sill to face a young woman, standing in dignified silence in front of a trembling old man. Instinctively Mu San glanced from her to Mo Tsen, comparing the two to the detriment of Mo

218

Tsen. Once this girl must have been as beautiful as Fu Fu, whom so many young students had dreamed of winning in young Chen's first year at Peking University. He felt fastidious distaste to see a girl, once as beautiful as Fu Fu, wearing the Lenin jacket. He blamed her for wearing such garb and thought that she looked old and worn. These things he could not forgive her, nor could he forgive her for showing no sign of fear, thus making his task the harder. "As a good citizen of the State I must report you," he said.

"And why?" she asked.

"Because you show pride. You still regard yourself as belonging to the long-gowned people, educated in the classics. Such superiority is not permitted."

"Report that to the State," she said. "Tell them also for me that the literati will bear watching. Someday the State will liquidate them as they now are liquidating the merchants. You will be among them. You do not fool me. I know what class you belong to."

"Hold your tongue. Call the head of the house." Angrily Mu San gave the command.

"He is not here," the girl answered, making no move to obey. "Nor is there any money or goods to collect."

"You lie! For this you must give account and for your rudeness." Mu San intended that she should be punished for compromising him before his group.

"Search the shop if you wish." Her voice was steady, her eyes hard and cold.

Young Chen looked across the high counter, the shelves behind were empty. Often in China a merchant's shop was thus stripped, but there was always treasure hidden some-where and he knew where such treasure was to be found. "Come," he said to the group. "And you," pointing at the girl, "lead the way."

Under her guidance the students, accompanied by the soldiers, walked through the empty court behind the shop. "Let us lift the loose stones in the second courtyard," Mu San ordered, stooping to lift one himself. But it was not loose! None were loose! And in all the rooms surrounding the various courts they met no one except the girl and the trembling servant who attended her. Finally they came to the last court, an untidy space littered with refuse, be-tween the house and the back wall, with a door leading to an alley. "I suggest we turn over these piles. Undoubtedly we'll find recently-dug earth beneath them." As he spoke Mu San was conscious that Mo Tsen and her friend were regarding him with suspicion. Did they think that he was simply making a show of finding the hidden money? He picked up a shovel leaning against the wall, determined to show that at least he was not above labor. "This is the common hiding place for greedy merchants," he cried out. But when the refuse was thrown aside, they found the earth was hard and it gave off a sour smell, indicating it had not been disturbed for years.

"Tell us where your father is hiding." Mu San spoke sternly to the girl, feeling the eyes of all the group upon him.

"I have no knowledge of where my father has gone," she answered, retaining her calm.

The police moved forward to arrest her, she had defied the State.

"Just a moment," said Mu San. "We have not finished the investigation. Girl, lead the way to the front of the shop," he commanded. "I wish to examine the inner room behind the counter. There is where your father is undoubtedly hiding."

Such a room was familiar to Mu San. In the long ago in just such a room his grandfather had weighed the silver taels at the end of the day. As they went through the courts to the front of the shop Mo Tsen, walking beside him, whispered, "Little brother, how did it happen you did not take us there in the beginning? It would have saved time if we had talked to the wicked capitalist first. Did you wish to give him time to escape? Are your thoughts right?"

Loud enough for all to hear, Mu San replied, "So far have I forgotten the ways of capitalism that I failed to remember the inner room."

When they had all gathered behind the counter, the daughter of the house pulled aside the bamboo screen which hung over a door.

A limp body hung from the rafters, the head fallen upon the chest.

"Leave me now that I may minister to my dead," she cried. "Time for burial is still granted by the State." As she entered the room and dropped the curtain behind her, none moved to follow her.

It was not many days before Mu San was made to realize that he had failed in the assignment, not because he had brought back no money; neither was the death of the middle-aged merchant held against him—suicides among the merchants speeded up the liquidation of the capitalist class which until it was completely destroyed would threaten the classless society. Not to have arrested the daughter who had defied the State was his crime. Mu San had hoped, since the soldiers, even Mo Tsen, had kept silent at the time over the matter, his leniency would not be reported to the authorities of the university.

Under the new government, society was divided into groups of ten and one member of each group belonged to another group and reported to it the actions of his own group. In this way Mu San was now to learn that every person's actions were not only known to his own ten, but were passed on to another ten. In the endless chain of reporting it was inevitable that he would be denounced for not seeing that the merchant's daughter was apprehended, and brought before the students and teachers to confess his error.

"I still bear the taint of my family's capitalistic thoughts. I have shown leniency toward that foul thing, capitalism. I should have arrested the daughter of the wicked merchant." Humbly he uttered the words.

Sitting upon the platform during the confession, Lo revelled in the humiliation which the proud youth, his former pupil, was being made to experience. Hereafter, to rectify such wrong thinking, Lo saw to it that all day and well into the night Mu San, in relation to his past and present, studied and discussed the absolute, correct solution handed to man in scientific Marxism. Professors and group members searched out his thoughts through his words.

"Love the State, love science, love the people (the right people)." Backward, forward—whatever the State said was right he must accept, but at night sometimes he dreamed of the proud girl—daughter of the merchant—not one of the right people, confusing her with Fu Fu. He would wake desiring her. How, now, to control his dreams?

Soon there filtered down from Lo to the group the suggestion that it would be well to harden this somewhat effete youth—let him supervise a band of children who also were to be hardened. Let him take children, who had never witnessed such a scene before, to see an execution, the group to watch the reaction of both Mu San and the children and report.

For a moment when the victim's head fell the children were held in a kind of catalyptic horror, unable seemingly to move hands or eyes. Then they broke and ran screaming. "Get them back," Mo Tsen commanded Mu San. "There is another to be killed." And he dared not disobey. This time the children laughed and young Chen felt an almost uncontrollable impulse to run away, get home, see if all was well with his own small brothers and sisters.

In the group meeting, the next day, the leader discussed the rightness of the act. Mu San did not join in the chorus of approval, hoping no one would notice. "You did not agree with the State, comrade?" Convicted by his silence, he remedied it by extravagant praise of the power of the State to shape little children.

"Now we will go forth to serve the *right* people," said Mo Tsen, who had recently become the leader of the ten. "We will build a cement trough by the well in the alley nearby the school in order that the women may stand erect when they do their washing instead of kneeling on the slimy stones, as they did under the foul government we have liquidated." Never before had Mu San engaged in heavy manual labor and he found it tiring, but strangely cleansing—cleansing him of guilt for the harm he felt he had done to the children the day of the executions. But at the next meeting when members of the group probed for his motive in helping to build the trough, he answered, "I felt pleasure in making easier the lot of the masses."

"You are again in error, little brother. You should feel only that you are happy to obey the State," they told him.

"I am in error," he murmured. Backward into cruelty, forward into kindness, Mu San was flung. When would his mind ever set to the pattern of the State?

The attention of his group was now focused on the résumé of his life which Mu San must write. In it he must expose everything in his entire life to public scrutiny. This dossier would be filed to use at any time by the State. His tension increased as more and more he felt his privacy assaulted by the group's effort to ferret out his every personal thought and feeling—all love for his family, all interest in study for its own sake, all inner conviction of what he had been taught was right and wrong. Doggedly he stripped away layer by layer the garments clothing his inner self. And yet the group was not satisfied.

Chapter 17

EVER SINCE THE MORNING
when young Chen had appeared with his tale of David
Conway's return to China, Lo had not been able to get
rid of his feeling that somehow the American, so unexpectedly brought back into his life, would destroy him.
As the days went by and no trace of David had been found,
his fear grew: suspicion might arise that he was helping
the foreigner; his boyhood association with David Conway, set down in Lo's dossier, might be re-evaluated in the
light of present happenings.

Across the table from Lo, at the first conference over
the foreigner's illegal entrance into the country and myste-

rious disappearance, had sat a woman high in the Party, indeed one of the most powerful. She was young, energetic, and ambitious. She alone in the hierarchy never wore the loose tunic and trousers, but instead a cleverly cut gown such as well-to-do women had formerly worn. Long pendants dangled from her ears. How does she dare, he had often thought, indignant that she set aside the ideal of "socialist man"—frugality, the simple life, individualism wiped out.

Lo had lived as consecrated a life as any priest. Not divorcing the wife his mother had forced upon him—although the new government countenanced such divorces, he had lived alone, a celibate, serving the State. Long ago he had come to hate this woman of the Party who flaunted before him the things of the flesh. She was beautiful and he still loved beauty. On the morning when he finished his recital of the foreigner's entrance into the country, she had smiled an enigmatic smile. He had looked away and raised his eyes to the picture of Mao Tse-tung hanging above him. Her eyes followed his. He had a sudden intuition that she would see to it that the hierarchy would be reminded of his former association with foreigners, arouse their suspicion of a possible connection between him and the foreigner. As scholar and teacher in the old regime he had done his own thinking. She would see that they asked among themselves now whether he had ever recovered from such individualism gained from his association with Americans—this American.

When at last David Conway had been found, partially by Lo's persistent efforts, Lo felt enormous relief. The man would be executed immediately; but instead the decision was made to hold Conway from public condemnation until they had a written statement of his intention to sabotage Shanghai's vital utilities. The tribunal meant to use such a statement to great effect in the campaign against America. Still latent in many of the minds of the people of the city was an unrealistic sense of friendship for America. That is why it had been necessary to get rid of the man Damon who had wormed himself into the people's emotions. Western teachers and doctors who had worked in this city for a hundred years had trained the Chinese to like them. Western businessmen had brought in many luxuries which the people liked. It had proved difficult to erase from the minds of the middle class the idea that Americans were not wholly evil. Now, at last, they had a prominent American whom they could use to show how traitorous Americans were. Born in China, all his life receiving its benefits, yet he had betrayed the country of his birth. When they received from Conway the statement of his guilt he would be subjected to the tribunal of public opinion; he would come before the people as the symbol of America's betrayal of friendly China.

It had then been arranged that throughout the day and late into the night groups should be used to soften the mind of the former banker. When it came to the choice of the groups, the woman Lo feared, dressed this time in a trim suit, a white flower on her coat lapel, offered a suggestion. "We are aware that one of our number declared in his dossier that he once knew this foreigner. Would he not be the one to handle the midnight interrogation? Playing upon the weaknesses of the American's past misdeeds, he could undoubtedly get a confession from the American at the hour when man's inner resources are lowest." As all eyes were turned upon Lo, the woman again smiled her enigmatic smile. Indeed, Lo was afraid.

In the days that followed groups of students, laborers and children came and went continuously outside David's lighted house. Sometimes they sang the songs of the Party. Sometimes, in a recitative singsong, they told of the accomplishments of the New China, of the peasants who now owned the land. They sang of the resources of industry and shipping, once in the hands of the West, so flagrantly used to benefit the West, now given to the people. They told of the vice allowed by the foreigners to exist in Shanghai. And they taunted David—"White man, foreign devil, bringer of opium to China. White man, white man stealing our ports—Hong Kong, Shanghai, Tientsin." The climax—"America, archenemy, giving arms to Chiang Kai-shek, fighting an imperialistic war in Korea."

Then came the midnight hours of interrogation and the effort to get a confession from the American. Lo had suggested to his group that it would be more effective if Conway did not know who was divulging his past. Lo would prepare the questions but other members of the group should undertake the interrogation. The questions at first were so framed that Lo did not involve himself. But when, night after night, the man showed no sign of weakening, Lo had to own he had underestimated David's powers of resistance and that he must make the questions more personal.

Why, after getting Damon to substitute for him, should Conway risk so much to rescue him? Over and over Lo asked himself this question, believing that once he solved the enigma he would be able to get a confession from David. Finally he came to the conclusion that it was a bourgeois sense of guilt which had actuated the foreigner. The man thought himself guilty of a crime, returning, as did all criminals in a capitalistic State, to the scene of the crime. He tried now to put himself in David's place and feel what guilt could do to a man. If Conway could feel guilt over letting Damon substitute for him, could not the same emotion be made to pervade the whole of his mind? Could he not in time be made to see his whole life as a betrayal of China, even believe he was a part of a plot to destroy Shanghai? Begin with his childhood, go on to things that had happened in his boyhood, things Lo knew and no one else did but which so far he had hesitated to tell. Once they were known, they might be used against Lo himself. But he could no longer hold back such details.

When the group next met, he suggested that, if they approved his plan, they question David on his childhood. The two who went to interrogate the American that night, in quiet gentle voices, sought to mire him in childish acts of betrayal, anger him, make him lose face, make him shout his denial. But the man remained calm! He did not shout. To all their questions he replied quietly, "Why ask these questions again? You know I was born in China."

"You had an amah. She was good to you? Were you always good to her? Did you not treat her children like inferiors?"

Ah, amah! Suddenly David remembered amah, he tormenting her, she chasing him but unable to catch him as she hobbled after him on her bound feet. "Ai yah! Shao Con, the young master is strong," she would cry and gloat over his ability to win over her. But when he broke long-established customs, she was the master and retribution was swift. The wholesomeness of their encounters made him smile at the memory. He felt strengthened.

Baffled by the effect on David when amah had been mentioned, Lo decided to take precious time from the few hours of sleep he had previously allowed himself to bring into sequence the events of David's youth which would be likely to make him feel guilt. He sought to revive the period in his life when he had been associated with David and his father. First there was the summer when he had gone with them to the Yellow River on an expedition. A tripod upon his shoulder—he had been forced to carry the load because the teacher insisted he learn the dignity of labor. How false the teaching! The American teacher, John Conway, was trying to make slaves of the Chinese people, make them into a nation of laborers for the use of imperialistic America! John Conway, an American, an unprincipled, religious humanitarian, who simulated the virtue of generosity in order to prepare the way for his banker son, David! Hot anger rose in Lo against both father and son. And then suddenly he seemed to feel the hot sun on his back; he and David were sitting together, and he was reading the beloved Chinese classics to his friend. From whence came such thoughts? Quickly he put them from him, centering his mind on the next summer when he had taken David to his home with him, and David, who had professed undying friendship for him, had deserted him at a critical moment. Desertion of his Chinese friend, desertion of Damon. Always betrayal. Surely the American would break when confronted with such actions.

That evening when he joined his group Lo asked first for a session of study so that he might rid himself of individualistic coloring, cleanse himself of that moment when he had thought kindly of Americans. That done, he said, "I have arranged another set of questions which can be used against the foreigner if the group agrees, but first let us soften this fellow with that sentimentality characteristic of his class. Let us appeal to his professed love of the city in which he was born—he used often to speak of it—then use these questions I have prepared."

That evening David, after having been taunted and reviled by various groups sent to the house during the day, was visited by two members from Lo's group who used with delicacy the stiletto of memory to disarm him: they spoke to him of Peking—did he not love the city, its beauty, the beauty of the house in which he had been born?

"Yes, I loved Peking."

Now the questions Lo had prepared were hurled at him in quick succession. Did he not recall friends of his youth, Chinese boys with whom he had studied? Why had he, an invited guest, been so impolite as to leave the house of a friend? Would you not call it desertion?

But these memories did not cause David to feel guilt, as Lo had expected. To be sure, he remembered the incident.

"I left only because my presence caused embarrassment to my friend," he answered.

Fear such as he had inflicted on others now gripped Lo. San Fan was a purge to weed out corruption from the men in power, rid the hard core of the Party of men like himself. Would not the fact that he still had not brought the foreigner to justice be interpreted as laxity on his part? More and more fearful of Party discipline, he renewed his efforts to trap David. What would be the particular event in the man's life, as Lo knew it, that would bring home to him his betrayal of China? Suddenly Lo's mind gave a leap forward to May thirtieth, nineteen-twenty-five. Surely the events of that day could be used to make David feel guilt, for it was then that he had been so deeply unfaithful to their mutual friendship.

Lo had been passing through Shanghai en route to his ancestral home on that day. Although he had sworn years before that he would never return, he was returning for the purpose of claiming his son, now seven years old. He wanted to get him out of the stultifying old-fashioned patriarchal life. He had gone by way of Shanghai, the longer route in order to see David Conway, who was back in China after six years in America. With difficulty and with shame, now Lo acknowledged to himself that at that time he had regarded this hated foreigner as a friend. Friend! A false conception! Could he ever have had such a relationship, and with an American? How was it that long before he had not recognized the American as an enemy of China? However, shameful as that relationship with

David was, he must go over in his mind the details of their meeting.

It was noon when the Tientsin boat docked. When he walked down the ship's gangplank and onto the pontoon, he was surrounded by friends. They were excited. They told him they were carrying banners that afternoon in a procession protesting the international authorities' unwarranted act of arresting Chinese laborers who had struck against the intolerable conditions in Japanese factories. One he did not recognize stepped forward. "Sixth Brother wishes to welcome honorable First Brother." The boy who was addressing him, it seemed, was his half brother, the son of one of his father's concubines. "Would elder brother have dinner with younger brother this evening after the parade?" Even now Lo could see the boy's eager, intelligent face.

Promising to meet him later, Lo had left his friends in order to attend to some business. On the way to his appointment he heard the news that a crowd of students had gone to the police station in the foreign concession to demand that the strikers who had been imprisoned should be freed. Policemen at the command of a British officer had fired on them. Lo's brother was one of those who had been killed.

Grieving for his brother, so intelligent, so ruthlessly shot down, Lo later had gone to the hotel where he had learned David Conway was staying. Yes, despite what had happened, he had sought out David Conway. He found it shameful to remember the fact, but he must in order to bring this imperialist, this traitor, to a realization of his guilt.

Little knots of foreigners were standing in the lobby entrance. Some were seated at small tables in the room beyond, drinking and casually discussing the shooting. Scattered bits of their conversation reached him. "It served them right." "The Chinese students have been out of hand for a long time." "There's a law against parades." "The law had to be upheld."

Choking with anger, Lo had started to leave the hotel, unmindful of his errand, when he found his way blocked by David. "How nice to see you, Lo. Won't you join my crowd?"

Join foreigners on such a day! Yet he had not pushed the fellow aside as he should have and left, instead he had said, "I have a message for you from your father, but I cannot deliver it here."

"Let's go up to my room," David answered. As soon as they were alone he had added, "I know how unfortunate this incident is, but surely, Lo, you who have studied the Western idea of justice know that the police were justified in firing."

Aghast at such words coming from a man who, only a few years before, had marched by his side to protest Western highhandedness, Lo had started to leave.

David had grabbed him by the shoulder, "Don't let's quarrel. Remember our pledge—we're brothers."

Oh, that Lo, the Communist, could wipe out the mingling of his own blood with that of this falsehearted foreigner! Sternly Lo reminded himself that the ancient rite was a superstition no longer accepted by Chinese Communists. It had no meaning. Ah, but he could use it to make

234

David conscious of guilt! The new doctrine taught that the State could make what it wished of plants, animals, and men. Control the environment, control David's environment.

Lo did not realize that in his effort to revive David's past environment he would revive his own. Memories poured in upon him. The day after he had seen David he had started on the trip up the Yangtse with the coffin of his younger brother in the hold of the steamer. His arrival in the city of his fathers. His brother's coffin borne through the gateway to the ancestral home, the sound of the women's keening, the furious beat of tom-toms, the clash of cymbals as the yellow-robed priests forced back evil from the stream of the living. He in sackcloth, the roughly woven white gown, the white band around his head, kneeling among the men of his family.

With difficulty he threw off the power of the family. His father was indolent, weak, an opium smoker, his mother unyielding, holding back progress. No hero in her eyes, this half brother who had died for the honor of China; she regarded him as a rebellious member of the family, even as she regarded Lo. He saw his mother as she looked when he had asked her for his son: clad in sackcloth, her high forehead covered with the coarse white band of mourning, her overlarge black eyes brilliant with anger, her imperious mouth set in a stubborn line—she, the ruler of the men in her household as well as the women, denied him the right to his own son!

"Bitterness! Bitterness!" she had cried, "You have brought humiliation upon me. And now you come asking that I commit to you the one boy who against your will you begot. You and he are the lineal descendants—a slim enough protection against disaster. You even refuse to enter the chamber of your wife and make possible another child to carry on the family. The one you have begot you shall not have. He must be trained to honor the graves of the ancestors, to offer them incense. I have seen to it that you shall not know, among the children of this household, which is your son. All are sworn to keep the knowledge from you."

There were three boys in the family about the age of his son. Which one was his? How could Lo know? He had never seen the boy. Now he sought out the woman he called wife and lay with her. She would not tell him which was his son. "I dare not," she whispered.

"I go then," he had said to his mother, and she had not sought to detain him. Now over him flowed the sense of isolation and despair that had gripped him that day when the gate of his ancestral home had closed behind him forever. He would go to the man who had been a real father to him. He could hear John Conway saying, "Your ancient teachers have laid upon you a great responsibility. Your traditions have much in common with the great tradition of America. You have your town fathers, we have our town meetings. Blend the best of yours and ours. Your local guilds go back into antiquity. Preserve, enlarge until you bring democracy to the very highest seats of government. Honor tradition—survival lies in a continuous, ever-developing process. Be patient."

It was John Conway who had voiced such ideas. An

American! It was such talk as this which had led to the
condoning of the killing of these Chinese students, his
brother among them! And David Conway, the son of this
man, had condoned the shooting, had talked of justice in
such killings! No! Lo never wanted to see his American
friends again. He would join the men of his country who
believed in a violent break with the past—a revolution
modeled on the Russian revolution. He would go to Mao
Tse-tung's home, hunt him out, learn more of the doctrine
of revolution. Mao's name was being mentioned more and
more among Communist thinkers. At present he was in
his native Hunan, the province of proud revolutionary
men, organizing the peasants in the doctrines of revolution.
Hunan lay not far to the south of Lo's home.

A brilliant, metallic sky shone over Hunan as Lo made
his way by sampan, by chair, to Mao Tse-tung's village.
No rain had fallen, and the parched rice was yellowing in
the paddies. Wherever there was a little stream, a pond,
he could hear the whine of the foot treadles trod by men
and women pumping the precious water into the fields.
Only now did Lo, a city man, taste the despair of the
peasant facing famine, for the rice crop of the previous
year had been commandeered by the retreating warlord.
Warlords came and went, each taking his toll of the
people's resources. "O China, thy sons must redeem thee!"
Lo had cried in his heart, even as he cried now.

Secretly, at night, he had sought out the farmhouse
where Mao Tse-tung was hidden, as a price had been
placed on his head by the governor for arousing the
peasants. The interview had been restrained at first—Mao

the peasant doubtful of Lo the city man. Then gradually suspicion changed to confidence. "The peasants," Mao explained, "possess the precious quality of energy." In them the revolution must be centered.

This meeting was a memory which Lo treasured—his one personal contact with the great Mao. Thin, sunburned, about him the air of a scholar, even then Mao showed his greatness, his originality, his courage to depart from the Russian pattern. "We have a different tradition from that of the Russians," he had said. "The urban worker cannot be at the center of our revolution." This was indeed daring! Who else would dare to criticize Marx? And with all, Mao could quote the Chinese classics with the fluency of an old-time scholar. It was his scholarly knowledge which he had used later to infuse with life the mechanized philosophy of the revolution—folklore, poetry, drama, put at the service of communism to rouse village after village to white-hot anger against the landlords and the imperialists, to tap powerful forces hidden deep in the mythology of the people, stimulate violent action so necessary to the revolution.

At the end, Mao had mentioned the name of Chou En-lai. He was behind the strike in Shanghai; Mao told Lo it was Chou who had roused the students to demonstrate. This memory, too, would not be denied. So the students had been manipulated by Chou En-lai, whom Lo did not trust. Confused, uncertain, he had gone back to Peking, and for some time longer he had listened to imperialist doctrines coming from the mouth of John Conway.

Lo had never confessed to this defection. He knew he

should now go before his ten and make a statement, telling how for a time he had reverted to capitalistic thinking, but he was fearful if he did so that, in the endless chain of reporting, it would reach the hierarchy. Instead, when his group met again for consultation over the prisoner, Lo suggested that after reminding him of his boyhood's exaggerated claims of loyalty to China, they suddenly confront him with the happenings of that day in 1925 when he had been so callous to the shooting of China's students by Western police.

Chapter 18

DAVID, IMPRISONED IN THE
lighted room, red-eyed from lack of sleep, half starved,
cold, unwashed, continued to withstand all the cleverly designed pressures to make him confess that he was a spy
come to blow up Shanghai's water system—an accusation
so absurd he felt nothing could make him confess to such
a crime, but he was becoming confused over the introduction of extraneous material. Strangely personal questions
having nothing to do with his illegal entrance into the
country, many of them centering around his father, more
and more often had been introduced into the late evening
interrogations—things of which the young men and women
interviewing him could have no knowledge.

Who was it who knew David's family intimately enough to give them such details to use against him? A friend? In this distorted world in which he now dwelt, China's gift for friendship was not nonexistent but had become an active force turned into evil. Who was the former friend using the intimate knowledge gained through friendship to destroy him? If he knew, David thought, he could better defend himself. There was one friend above all others—it couldn't be Lo!

The days passed. A week? Two? A month? David hardly knew.

The questioning went on. "Why did you leave China? You called this country your own, but as soon as you were old enough to decide for yourself, you left it, did you not?"

"Yes."

"And you came back."

"Yes."

"You did not join your father as you had promised him you would."

"He did not exact such a promise."

"You mean your father prepared the way for you to join the capitalists who were exploiting China?"

"My father had nothing to do with my decision to go into business in China. My father begged me to join the mission school in which he was teaching."

"So you defied your father. How do you account for that? You have posed as one who always obeyed the Chinese concepts taught you in your childhood?"

What could he answer? he thought wildly. To say his father had given him his blessing to go into business would

241

be interpreted as connivance on the part of a missionary to bring China under the dominance of capitalism. If he said his father did not wish him to go into business, they would accuse him of tearing down a Confucian concept— the father-son relationship. So they tightened the noose.

"You came back to take part in the capitalist exploitation, didn't you?"

"International trade is what countries live by," David answered.

"Give me the date you returned to China."

"Nineteen-twenty-five."

"The day of the month."

"May. The exact date I don't remember."

"Tell me what happened here in Shanghai on May thirtieth."

When David did not answer, the interrogator nudged his memory. "There were shootings in the city that day."

"What has that to do with me?" David cried out.

"A great deal. You were very callous, were you not, to what happened to Chinese students?"

He was silent. Channels of memory began opening up. The historic events, of course, he remembered. Writ large in every white man's mind was the beginning of the great boycott of foreign products. But what had *he* done on that day that could have offended his friend? He struggled to remember. *He must remember*. He tried to stand outside the present, go back to that May day. Each time his mind veered off. Then suddenly he remembered what had happened on May thirtieth, nineteen-twenty-five. This was the last time he had seen his friend Lo, who had come to see him at the hotel, and David had asked him to join him in a drink with his American friends. Just to ask a Chinese to do such a thing, on a day when every white man in the city was disgusted with the students for threatening the police, was a definite gesture of friendship, but Lo had refused to join them.

"Suppose we go up to my room," David remembered saying, for he wanted to talk with his old friend. He remembered apologizing for the disorder in the room. "I'm packing to go upriver. I am to be assistant manager of the American shipping firm with headquarters in your city. I hope that means we'll see something of each other."

Lo had expressed no pleasure in his friend's news. Instead he had said, "Although this is a very difficult occasion for me, in order to bring a message from your revered father, I have put aside my own grief and the grief of my people in what has happened today."

"Aren't you taking it pretty hard?" David had asked. "We are not schoolboys any more. Let's look at it as grown men. It's a pity some students were killed, but they were definitely breaking the law. What would have been the result if they had got hold of the rifles in the station house? The police only did their duty."

"Wind past the ears," Lo had cried. "You foreigners shoot down scholars as if they were criminals. You, who were born and bred in the ancient Confucian Code, know that the scholar is above the law. He is governed by ethical restraint."

"A minute ago you were treating me like a foreigner;

now, when it serves your purposes, you use my Chinese birth to confound me."

"So you no longer wish to be identified with the country of your birth and the lofty principles of its scholars?"

"You call breaking into a police station scholarly restraint?" David flung back, holding up his end of the argument as he always had with Lo in the past.

"My younger brother died today. He was one of the students."

"Forgive me, Lo," David had hastened to say. "I didn't know you were personally involved in this. I'm sorry."

"He died in protest against imperial oppression," Lo had answered, ignoring the apology.

"It was good of you to bring the message from my father at such a time."

Thinking back to that conversation, David believed he had spoken gently, hoping to lessen his friend's anger against him. For a little he thought he had, for Lo sat down saying, "Your honored father thought I might convey to you what he was unable to put into words. He has honored me with his confidence. In the years you have been away he has treated me as a son. I lived in his house for a time when my funds were low . . . one scholar helping another. He has sought to teach me the ideals of democracy, a social philosophy he calls it, but he says you are needed if his work is to succeed."

Lo, as he spoke, had rested upon the table his beautifully shaped hands, typical of the scholar, delicate, well controlled by a lifetime of training in the use of the writing brush. There on the left wrist was a tiny scar. There was a

244

like scar on David's left wrist. "Lo," he exclaimed, "you have been a son to my father in my absence. When you go back to Peking, will you undertake, in the name of our relationship as brothers, to make clear to my father my love for him—but that I must choose my own way of life?"

Then Lo had risen, bowed formally, saying, "You do me a great honor, but I am not returning to Peking at present. I go to the house of my fathers, taking with me the dead body of my younger brother for burial."

And now, after all these years, it came to David that his father might not have sent Lo. It was not like his father to try to coerce him. Could it be that Lo had invented the message as an excuse to come to see his boyhood friend, hoping to find in the old personal relationship the kinship with democratic principles which at heart he believed in? Did he want support? If I had understood his grief—yes, and his anger—could I have steadied him while the storm of anger was sweeping his country and mine farther and farther apart? Did I fail him? Could it be that I turned Lo toward communism?"

As the days went by and the questions asked of David entangled him more and more in this and that act committed in the past, he grew distrait. Could he cope with both the present and the past? Could he withstand the double assault? Would the confession they sought to get from him become confused in his mind with that feeling growing within him that he had failed his friend Lo when he had most needed him? Could he then be made to give evidence against his own country? His betrayal of Damon confused him still further. Voices, voices—he scarcely knew

whether they came from without or within—his desertion
of his first friend, Lo; his desertion of Damon; his desertion of China.

"Born in China, unfaithful to China, unfaithful to your
friends." Surely these were voices outside the room.

And close at hand a cultivated voice was asking, "Did
you not enter China to help destroy this new government?
Who sent you?"

Chapter 19

AT NOON, AND AGAIN IN THE
evening, everyone including Mu San's group met in factory, shop, school, office—cells directly linked one into another, to higher and higher levels, finally to Mao Tse-tung,
the great father of his people. Never before in all the world
had there been such mass conversion, six hundred million
mindless people, swayed by the mind of one man, one idea.

The cohesive mass for a long time had been aquiver
with one purge after another. Many had been exposed and
punished. Some had been sent to hard labor to help bring
about Chinese industrialization, others executed. No district, scarcely a family, remained untouched. The young,

247

feeding upon the excitement and importance they had attained in the right to inform on parents and teachers, had brought many parents to justice—a praiseworthy act to expose a loved one in error. Christian and Confucian mothers and fathers alike feared the moment when small children would be old enough to speak, lest they report words overheard of Christian or Confucian ideals; but even these parents felt pride when the announcement came from Korea that China, which had lost in so many wars, was now triumphing over the Westerners. Patriotism was a new and terribly moving experience.

But recently there were those, even among the young, who were grieved over the punishment they had brought upon a father, a mother, a sister, a brother; a few, who had been made to administer the beating which brought death to a member of the family, had committed suicide. Some strange new sensation of guilt unforeseen by the hierarchy was affecting the people. The collective body was losing some of its driving force.

Joy and laughter must again be instilled in the unthinking body. From on high came the news, filtering down from cell to cell, that now the purges were over everyone was happy. Such happiness could no longer be held within bounds; everyone demanded a parade. The noon hour, instead of being given over to study, was now given over to learning the new dances. In the streets and the alleyways men and women and children danced the new steps accompanied by the beating of drums and cymbals. Old and young laughed and sang.

Mu San forced himself to dance with the others, but

he was filled with a deep anxiety. He wished to belong to the Communist Party. He wanted to give himself so completely to the State that he would be received into its hard core. This demanded the utmost soul-searching linked to abstract theory. This written résumé of his inner life must be read in public. In some magic way he felt he would then be released from his past. But would his confession be accepted? Could he make it reach to the depths of his soul? He was making a supreme effort to expose to view his past life: his childhood, education, family relationships, friendships. In this effort to enter into the mystic union with collective man, he must divest himself of his individuality, be submerged in the sea of universality.

Group parties, family parties were being allowed in preparation for the great parade. Those who had jewels were urged to wear them and the Lenin jacket could be discarded for silks or satins. But those who had jewels and silks hesitated to bring them out. Might they not later be denounced for hiding riches from the State? But gradually one after another relaxed, caught up into the mass joy. Even Mu San felt less burdened with anxiety. On the day before the parade, all morning he worked happily with the others in decorating the assembly hall of the university. He pasted hundreds of Picasso doves of peace, cut out of white paper, on the walls. He mounted a ladder and fastened to the ceiling wires attached to papier-mâché doves. Climbing down from the ladder, he observed with satisfaction how the doves floated above the enormous pictures of Stalin and Mao.

Everyone was given the afternoon to spend with his

family. Mu San, having no family in the city and hoping to forget how much he missed them, ensnared by the seeming laxity of discipline today, thought to go over to the university he hoped to enter after his indoctrination was completed—if his confession was accepted. A professor in medicine whom he had known in Peking was teaching there, or so he had been told in Hong Kong. Mu San had thought he might possibly be allowed to study medicine— because the course now given was only two years in length, he could quickly be trained to work for the State. Lonely and now again oppressed with his coming ordeal, he sought by this visit to get back some of the relief he had felt while decorating the hall.

When he reached the campus he asked a group of students to direct him to the office of Dr. Sen. "We don't know him," they answered and hurriedly walked away.

Mu San walked on, unaware of steps behind him until a hand was laid on his shoulder. He turned to face his old teacher, Lo; this was the first time they had talked with each other since the morning Mu San had arrived in Shanghai!

"The State's all-seeing eye followed you here. Why are you not among your comrades, little brother?" Gently the question was asked, but Lo's eyes were like points of steel.

"I took a minute to see the professor under whom I hoped I might study when my indoctrination was completed."

"You would decide how to serve the State?" demanded Lo.

"I am in error," murmured Mu San, his head bowed.

"The man you are looking for is no longer here. He, too, chose how he would serve the State."

"Does the State discard our scientists?" exclaimed Mu San, realizing even as he spoke that he was in real danger and yet he could not immediately surrender all his ideas of objective study.

"The students who are allowed to come here understand the partisan character of science—that science must serve a political purpose. Science, as Dr. Sen regarded it, has capitalistic overtones. He was an authority in bourgeois diseases. We are not interested in the diseases which attack the bourgeoisie. Dr. Sen insisted on perpetuating his own conception of medicine."

Mu San now knew that Dr. Sen had either been executed or sent to hard labor, and that for himself there would be a like fate if he did not quickly surrender his total self. "What do you want of me?" The young man's voice was little more than a whisper.

Lo, looking upon this young man whose sensitive mouth was contorted in an effort to control his horror over Dr. Sen's fate, whose nostrils flared in nervous reaction to pressures bearing down upon him, let out a hoarse cry of delight. "Ah, you have erred again! It is not what I, the servant of the State wants, it is what the State wants."

Looking at his old teacher, Mu San beheld a man possessed by some unhuman spirit. His hair, since their last meeting, had been cut short—as Mao now wore his—revealing Lo's pointed ears. Combined with his pointed chin and his expression of diabolic delight over his former pupil's predicament, he appeared to Mu San like a fox spirit, feared by all Chinese in their childhood. Mu San was terrified. Idle to tell himself fox spirits did not exist.

Seeing how frightened Mu San was, Lo walked away exhilarated, taken out of himself, caught up into the glory of vicarious suffering. He had driven the knife of fear deep into his former student. Suddenly he had an idea: this young man could be used to drive fear deep into the American and gain a confession—one driven man confronting another driven man.

It had been no accident that Lo had come upon his former student this afternoon. Lo, whose duty it was to supervise the initiates at the indoctrination school, had been watching Mu San for some weeks. Often when the time for a person's written résumé of the past drew near, a boy or a girl teetering between the old and the new could not endure the split between past and present and would either have to be put away in an asylum or would commit suicide. A promising convert was then lost to the State. This, Lo did not intend to have happen to so valuable a youth as Mu San. Of late Mo Tsen, the leader of his group, had reported that young Chen had been nervous and tense. Hate for the foreigner would save Mu San from his own destruction and drive him as no others had been driven to get the prisoner's confession.

The next morning before the parade Mu San was informed, through his group, that he was to interrogate David Conway, the spy, between twelve and two that night. Directly after the parade he was to go to the house of the Supervisor of the Indoctrination of Students, Comrade Lo, to receive his instructions.

The crowds that lined the streets applauded as the floats went by. What could be dearer to the Chinese people than floats: for centuries papier-mâché figures had been a part of official funeral processions—slaves, servants, concubines to attend the dignitaries in the other world. A great float moved by, a huge papier-mâché white hand rested on a platform erected on the chassis of an automobile, the fingers of the hand curled around the figure of a man. A banner read, "The agent of the State in the hands of the people." "Ai yah!" exclaimed an old woman in the crowd. "Ai yah! Now do I understand! We serve the State now, give our rice—even our sons in Korea—in order that the new government may serve us after death."

Now came a float on which a worker to be honored above all others stood alone—a young peasant woman, medals upon her breast, serious and docile of mien, a wondering look in her eyes. She had been raised to a place of honor because she had surpassed all her fellows in production. She, honored for the extra number of spindles she had been able to tend in the cotton factory where she was employed.

A band of young pioneers, their scarfs fluttering, swung into the procession, singing with all their might,

"See our banner, our victorious banner,
    and see the radiant sun rising in the East.
Hai, hai!
Six hundred million people cheer and sing.
We have Father Mao Tse-tung
To lead us in our march of liberty.

253

Behold, oh, behold, our beloved, beloved
Motherland."

Suddenly hundreds of white doves circled and swooped
overhead, their wings bright in the sun, whistles fastened
to their tails. "Ai yah! Ai yah!" broke forth in tremendous
volume from the throats of the people.

And now came the Yang-ko dancers, with painted red
cheeks, in yellow cotton trousers, bright red jackets, peasant scarfs on their heads, green sashes holding their drums
in place. They advanced to the rhythms, centuries old—
forward, backward, they moved in the pantomime of sow-
ing the grain. For centuries men's hearts had stirred to the
creative emotion the dance symbolized—man producing his
kind, earth producing man's nourishment. The drums beat,
cymbals clanged.

Mu San danced and sang, holding back his fears.

Curfew, and the city grew quiet. Mu San, unable entirely to get rid of the fear that the fox spirit had entered
Lo, stood trembling before him to receive instruction for
the evening. "Run over these questions, use them to con-
fuse the prisoner over his acts committed in youth and
manhood. Then accuse him of being a spy. A man's resistance is low during the hours from twelve to two," Lo
explained, adding, "These hours are your nightly assignment until you get a statement from him. He is stubborn.
It may take several nights. Since you will be returning to
the hostel at the university long after curfew, the State
gives you this paper to show the police if they accost you.
Now, go."

Young Chen took the last tram across the city from Lo's house in Chapei to David's in the former French Concession. Since there was still time before he was due at the house of the foreigner, he got off the tram at the People's Plaza, once the foreigners' race course. Here he would spend the extra moments walking under the willows. Here he hoped to gain strength to perform the task set for him. As he walked along the winding paths he found himself thinking of his grandfather's garden which was not far away. He longed to know what had happened to it under the new government, and then he seemed to be walking in that garden listening to his grandfather's words, "harmony between the opposing forces." Would memory never die? He hurried from the willow-bordered paths and along the empty streets to the house of the foreigner.

His heart beat fast as he entered the house where the man David, friend of his father and grandfather, was imprisoned. But at sight of the foreigner sitting on the edge of his cot, all sense that he had betrayed his grandfather and father's friend left Mu San. Surely they had been mistaken in showing friendship to such a monkey-hearted man! How quickly he had lost the look of a gentleman! The real quality was not in him. Mu San could despise this fellow, wearing a dirty jacket and trousers, sneakers worn down at the heels, unshaven, red-eyed—a mere travesty of the man his father and grandfather respected.

"Please stand," he commanded.

Slowly David rose, and when he saw who had come to question him he began to tremble. He felt that the foundations of society, as he had known them, were crumbling away. Friendship, loyalty gone! How could man survive without them? An abyss yawned before him.

"Why should I hold to loyalty when no one else does?" Then, horrified, he whispered in his heart, I will not betray my country. The deeds of which voices all day had accused America were not acts committed by his country. America held no treaty ports; America was not the bringer of opium to China. America had demanded the Open Door. America had sent to China, depleted by Japan's occupation, food, penicillin, even when it was scarce in America.

And now a single voice, close to him, Mu San's voice, asked, "Was America not guilty of dropping the atomic bomb on those whose skins are not the color of yours? Did you not spare the European whose skin coloration is like yours?"

David's head sank lower and lower.

"Do you own your country is guilty?"

"I—" he said and stopped.

"Go on."

"I—" again he stopped.

"In this awful act, surely you see your guilt."

A cry rose in David's throat. He, the representative of the white man's guilt, he who had guilts of his own, things come out of his childhood, youth, manhood to weaken him in this hour of crisis.

"Confess."

Damon! Paul Damon! He was guilty of Paul Damon's death. He was becoming confused. His own guilt? His nation? The white man's? If he could get rid of the lights all around him. Then anger helped him, anger against Mu San. Guilt! Mu San accusing him of guilt! Mu San was guilty of betraying his father!

But he, David, had betrayed Paul Damon. If only he confessed it, he would find peace. Lower, lower his head sank. And then in his moment of despair he felt sustained by, of all men, Paul Damon. He was David's substitute, a representative of Christendom who had accepted death rather than betray his country. Now he, David Conway, would walk in his substitute's shadow, even unto death. David's father also had accepted death. "Though I walk through the valley of the shadow of death, he will not fail me." Lifting his shoulders, but slowly as if he carried a great weight, David spoke, "You do not know what you ask, Mu San."

What had happened? This unkempt, abject man almost groveling, ready to confess, had suddenly stood erect and addressed his accuser as an equal. "You'll stand until you apologize for the effrontery of calling me by my first name." Young Chen could scarcely contain his anger.

The minutes passed—ten—twenty. David swayed, fell.

Looking at the fallen white man, Mu San tasted the joy of breaking a man, a strange new kind of pleasure. It was two o'clock. He must leave, but tomorrow night or the next or the next he'd make this once proud banker suffer torment for every misdeed the white man had ever committed, but he'd do it with politeness. "The artists and scholars are the 'spiritual workers,' " Lo had said. "As one of that number, do not demean yourself by shouting. The refined ways of the scholar, grace and subtlety, can be used as delicate stilettoes to prick the pride and self-respect of this man."

Suddenly, as Mu San was walking down the drive that led out of the foreigner's garden, he felt physical revulsion for what he was doing. Hurrying from the sight of the guards into the shrubbery, he vomited. Finally, spent and exhausted, he leaned against a tree, waiting for his strength to come back.

"Ah," said a voice out of the darkness, "are you not equal to the task the State has set for you?" Lo's voice.

Throughout the days that followed, Mu San struggled to complete the written document which would lay bare all thoughts and acts of his former life. Each time he thought it completed, some member of his group would suggest he had not fully surrendered his past. Driven on by anxiety that he would never be able to accomplish such a confession, Mu San found relief in planning how to make the hated foreigner sign the statement that he had come to Shanghai to destroy it. In tormenting David, Mu San was relieved of his own torment. But night after night young Chen failed to gain what he sought from David. He was in despair. Then an idea came to him—an inspiration— make this foreigner lose face, show him what he had become, strip him of the armor of self-respect. If he sees how low he has fallen, then he cannot fail to confess his guilt.

When Mu San told his plan to Lo, Lo said, "It is good. Go then and make your arrangements." Now Lo saw that he had created in this proud young man his own dark ecstasy in power through refined cruelty, and he was angry that the young Chinese had so soon learned this exquisite pleasure. It was too soon; he had not yet earned such ecstasy.

The next morning word came to Mu San that he was on that very afternoon to try again, before students and faculty, to make a satisfactory report on his past. There, with all their eyes upon his, he strove, even unto utter humiliation, to lay bare his soul. Lo, who was among those to pass judgment, deemed the document inadequate. Now Mu San must go through it all again, go deeper into the revealing of himself. There was but one thing left to reveal—he had not yet spoken of Third Uncle and the family graves. Would redemption come to him in such degradation?

Chapter 20

THAT NIGHT MU SAN CAR-
ried through his plan to show David how degraded he had
become. He asked Mo Tsen to help him. Between them
they carried a full-length mirror and placed it opposite the
prisoner who, with bowed head, was sitting on the edge of
his cot.

"Will you please stand?" Young Chen's voice was suave.
David rose. In so doing he faced his own image. The
stain on his face and neck, put there by the man who was
now tormenting him, was worn off in patches, showing
with startling effect his white skin. His hair was white at
the roots, but the telltale black of his disguise was like a

dirty cap on the top of his head. His beard was streaked with dirty white. His cotton jacket and loose trousers were rumpled, dirty and stained by the needs of his body. Shame, terrible shame, filled him. He was stripped of all semblance of human dignity! No longer was he a man who could command respect. "My God!" The words were wrenched from him.

Mo Tsen giggled. "So, now you see yourself. Are you pleased? A fine fellow, aren't you?" Young Chen laughed lightly.

The questioning began. To Mu San's delight, he found David's answers more confused, uncertain, than they had ever been before. But enough of the man's stubbornness persisted that a confession could not yet be wrung from him.

"I will leave with you the written statement of your guilt. I suggest you sign it before I come tomorrow night."

Mu San was no longer in a hurry. The infliction of pain on a member of the hated white race in some mysterious way restored his own precious face. Face, the new government did not consider that a Communist possessed such a thing as face. The integrity and privacy of the individual soul must be surrendered to the State. But Mu San, from the day he was born, had been surrounded by men and women who had at all costs preserved face, believing that a man's strength lay in preserving the outward coverings of his inner self! Thus only could a man live.

As soon as his tormentors had left, David flung from him the paper left him to sign. Avoiding the mirror, he began circling the room along the path which had been laid out for him—two feet away from the windows, four feet from the door. He must find some way to get rid of himself. As a small child, the houseboy, his Chinese teacher, amah, all had taught him that man cannot live without face. It was the precious clothing of his inner self. Before his enemies he had been stripped of all self-respect.

Around and around he went. He had no knife to use to kill himself, no way in the lighted room to hang himself. Round and round. Finally it penetrated his mind that a window was being raised. Had Mu San come back to witness his shame? Was Lo looking at him, laughing at him? He stopped, unable to go forward. Then he heard his name spoken. "Shao Con." An old woman's voice—a voice of the woman who had cared for him in childhood? "Shao Con." The name she called him by . . . he heard the words clearly, "Shao Con." A low pleased cackle came from outside the window. "We fool them. The honored one will cleanse his body, then put on the dirty clothes they force upon him. They will not know it, but his face will be restored to him." Now a small piece of soap was laid on the window sill. For a moment David saw the heavily veined hand of an old woman. She who had always cared for him? "Cleanse yourself while the guards sleep."

He obeyed. Hurriedly he washed in the lavatory, fearful that the guards might wake, yet somehow certain they wouldn't. Lying again on his cot, with the self-respect which cleanliness brings, he felt a cleanliness of spirit. And he felt sheltered. From the darkness beyond his windows someone who cared what happened to him had spoken. Had the old woman who had watched over him from childhood come back to look after him? Scenes from his childhood came to him—physical sensations of security and warmth—he, borne upward in his father's arms, his mother's warm fingers clasped around his, and somewhere out of time the words "in the secret place of the Most High."

A blessed silence filled the room, and he was shut off from the menacing world by the winter rain falling on the leaves of the trees in the garden. In his childhood his Chinese teacher had taken him into the hills and taught him how to sit quietly contemplating the wondrous world around him. Man, tiny, but a part of the universe, partaking of its grandeur. And now, even imprisoned as he was, humiliated as he was, he took on stature, one element necessary in the harmony of the universe.

Now, bulwarked by the quietude of the East, harbored in the physical security of his childhood, he could consider with calmness Mu San's last question, "Why did you go into shipping on the Yangtse on your return to China?" The Yangtse—out there in the wide universe it flowed. He seemed to be a small, but significant figure, such as always appeared in ancient Chinese pictures, standing upon a mountainside among the crags and peaks of the Yangtse, and down below he saw the river in all its beauty, all its grandeur, cutting its way to the sea. The towering cliffs rose above the tumultuous waters in great black masses. Plunging down them were the mountain streams, great sheets of water swollen in the spring, dyed with the red and yellow silt, mingling with the waters of the river. Crash and roar of cataracts, noise and turmoil of rapids, shouts from hundreds of men straining on ropes pulling the junks over the rapids, commands, curses, prayers,

"Save life, save life
O River Supreme."

In thousands of years the yellow men living upon the banks had not conquered the river, but the white man had. He had put steamers upon those turbulent waters, done away with the animallike labor of men straining on ropes pulling the junks over the rapids, and he, David Conway, the imprisoned American, had been a respected part of that noble struggle.

He remembered that on his way to his post on the upper river he had stopped at Nanking to see a friend. From the windows of the house he had looked upon the panorama of the lower river. On its wide waters steamers were moving, some of their bows pointed toward Shanghai, others pointed upriver. Away on the horizon, north and south, wraiths of smoke drifted from the smokestacks of the steamers before they disappeared over the rim of the horizon—smoke, the far-flung banner of international trade. The initiative, the courage of the men of the West was his heritage. He had been a factor in Western shipping. He, David Conway, was no longer a man cowering in shame. The memory of his own work strengthened him, he a participator in the life of the river, the life of China.

When Mu San returned the next night he found his victim curiously changed. He was no longer confused, uncertain. He stood facing his image almost with pride. "What was my part in the exploitation of your shipping? 'All countries have trade, must have trade to live. Trade's decent. Trade's good!' I am using the words of an old river captain," David explained, "the American, the dreamer, who put steamers on the upper river. He it was who replaced with two hundred-horsepower engines men swinging like monkeys on the end of crossbars taking junks over rapids. You delude yourself, Mu San, when you call it exploitation."

"Do not use my name! Say comrade," commanded Mu San, with great difficulty maintaining his calm.

"I wish it were comrade," David answered without hesitation. Then the young Chinese, unable longer to contain himself, heaped curses upon David, obscene Chinese curses.

As night after night the prisoner withstood every attempt to get him to sign the paper acknowledging America's traitorous acts, always answering the questions quietly and without malice, each night seeming more able to resist confession, Mu San began to think of David as his nemesis. Somehow this foreigner was holding him back from entering into mystic union with the Party. He was haunted with a premonition that his fate was tied up with the foreigner's fate. Until he secured David's confession he would not be able fully to divest himself of his past.

Feverishly day after day Mu San sought to tear to pieces the last shreds that were left of loyalty and love for his father, his mother, even for the girl Fu Fu. Yes, at last he confessed his love for her, for she scorned communism. It did not matter. She was either dead or had fled. Finally he informed on Third Uncle. He felt wrecked, destroyed, and yet it seemed he had not done enough. He begged the collective body to point out his errors.

After each meeting, accepting humbly the criticism, he would try again to write a more complete résumé of his past. Striving to destroy his former self, and yet seeking in some way he could not fathom to preserve that self, he would stop his writing to listen to the cadences of the pile-drivers' song as they worked on one of the new buildings the State was putting up. "Down, down, drive the great weight!" Then he would close his eyes and try to drift into the selfless state he longed for and could not seem to reach.

If he could make the foreigner convict himself, deliver himself to public humiliation, then only would the glorious vision of the new State, man complete in man, be given to Mu San. But how to find the weak point in Conway's armor. If only Mu San could use physical torture! But Lo had forbidden him to do so, saying, "In the eye of the people, his humiliation will be far greater if they believe he made his confession willingly through his own sense of guilt. Also, the spiritual workers are above such crude methods."

Mu San began to think that the flaw in his approach was that he had not brought group action to bear on his problem. Lo had not suggested it, probably waiting for Mu San to grasp his own error. Mu San consulted Mo Tsen. "Yes," she told him, "you have been in error. Let us plan together."

The next evening into the foreigner's room came Mo

Tsen. Curiously she surveyed this unkempt foreigner, asked him embarrassing questions, laughing delightedly at his answers. Then at the clap of her hands, girls in their early teens clad in slacks and Lenin tunics entered the room. Around David they moved like harpies, their black pigtails flying, taunting him. "See what you have become! You're dirty! Whew!" they cried, sweeping by him, out onto the veranda, back again, picking at his soiled garments. "A white man in rags." They laughed with glee. Around and around they circled, taunting him.

Beneath his ragged and dirty garments, David was conscious of the cleanliness of his body, and he stood quietly at the center of the revolving figures, looking somberly at one, then another. They know not what they do, he thought—naughty children such as he had known in his youth, calling him "foreign devil" to make him angry.

At last, when he showed no sign of breaking, Mu San spoke and the figures dancing wildly a moment before were still. "Prisoner, what part did you play in nineteen-twenty-seven when Nationalist Chinese troops marched down the Yangtse bent on unifying all China? You were on the upper river in the nefarious business of robbing the Chinese of their own shipping, were you not?"

"I was engaged in international shipping at that time," David answered.

"Think," commanded Mu San.

It was, oh, so long ago, a quarter of a century—wearily David forced his mind to remember the spring of 1927. Spring, and up from Canton to the Yangtse had marched the Nationalist troops, a boiling heterogeneous, revolutionary mass commanded by Chiang Kai-shek, who accepted the help of Russians, conservative Chinese officers, men of the old order, young men, hidden members of the Communist Party, peasants ready to fight for the ownership of their fields, all united in one desire to rid the country of the white man. "Drive out the white man, whether capitalist or missionary. Kill them, and prosperity will be ours."

"I rose above my own interest then." David whispered the words to himself. He had volunteered to go alone into the hinterland, warn the missionaries and businessmen in isolated stations, escort them down to the Western ships on the river. He had done it several times, leading small bands in the night down to the Yangtse, and the Chinese who had not been swept up into the mass hatred had helped him. Amidst all the hatred engendered on both sides, he had been one to preserve some measure of understanding between West and East.

And then he remembered that nothing anyone did had stayed for long the onrush of nationalism, and foreign shipping was driven from the Yangtse River. He had been on the last steamer to come down from the hinterland. While the ship lay at anchor at Nanking, he had gone ashore and quite unexpectedly had met his father at the house of a mutual friend. He could see his father clearly as he had looked that day, the same awkward man he always had been, and homely—an odd assemblage of features, delicate nose slightly crooked, long upper lip, but the eyes were beautiful—gentle and understanding.

Dimly at first, then more clearly, the scene came back— he and his father standing together by the window look-

ing out at the wide stretch of the lower river now bare of
ships. The sun was sinking. The river, the rice marshes, the
moat were a succession of red-dyed waters encircling the
massive city wall, a great undulating precipice never ending, flowing on to the right, to the left, hemming them in—
Hemming me in! Not a wall. A room! This room, guards
stirring outside! Again terror!

Then out of the years came his father's words. "What
you have done up river to keep understanding between
China and the West makes me proud." His father's trust
in him needed now. "You have shown patience and understanding, my son. This agony of China's is the West's
agony, too." We have helped to bring this fanatical nationalism upon China. The white man has been greedy.
Instead of instructing the Chinese in the use of our tools,
we have often used them to our advantage, to further our
power. "We must not desert them now."

"But they hate us. We've got to face it," David had
protested.

"Not all of them," his father had answered. "I have
come here because the students asked me to come and
steady them in their belief in democracy."

"But most of the students have turned from democracy
to communism," David had again protested.

"We have stirred the Chinese to Western concepts,
given them the knowledge of the Christian world, brought
them our inventions. It is for them a time of instability:
the old is slipping; the new is not firmly grasped. Many of
the students are fascinated with the offer of a heaven on

earth which the Russians promise them—China quickly transformed into an industrial nation."

David remembered asking his father, "Has Lo been carried away with such a vision?"

"I do not know. Sometimes I fear he has." His father's voice was full of pain.

Side by side they had stood silent, looking down the river. The light faded and all they could see was the sheer drop of the city wall and the lonely rice marshes, their waters black and forbidding. "Come with me to Shanghai," pleaded David.

"I cannot. The Chinese students asked me to join them here in prayer."

Two days later the troops, inflamed with hatred against the white man, entered Nanking. "Kill the white man!" It was no longer merely a slogan—missionaries, diplomats were shot. David's father, shot.

Now David forgot that his father had advocated tolerance. Hatred rose in him to meet the hatred of Mu San. "It is you who are guilty," he cried, pointing a trembling finger at his tormentor. "What did the Nationalist Army do in nineteen-twenty-seven? You Chinese killed my father who never harmed you."

Mu San, in fury, forgot his instructions. Pushing aside the band of girls, he struck David.

"You can't hide behind your failure. You lived in Shanghai from nineteen-twenty-seven until nineteen-fifty. What did you do to help China, which you professed to love? You feel no guilt for your life in Shanghai? What did you do all those years to help China? Answer me!" shouted Mu San.

"What would you expect me to do? Help the men who killed my father?" David remembered how in grief and anger, as the troops advanced upon Shanghai, he had stood rifle in hand behind barbed wire and sandbags erected on the outskirts of Shanghai's International Settlement and looked out into the hinterland of China torn with strife and determined to have nothing more to do with China. He had been cynical when Chiang, at last in control of a large part of China, had sought to purge his Party of the Communists and drive the Russians out of the country. How Chiang Kai-shek, who was seeking to unify China, succeeded was of no interest to David. He was cynical over Chiang's reforms. "A new China," he had scoffed along with other Westerners. "What are a few new bridges and roads?" That some of his father's former pupils, now high in the Nationalist Party, were struggling to establish a democracy he would not believe. "What can one expect?" he had said when luxury and the old evil squeeze began to creep in among the officials at the new capital of Nanking.

Trying to forget his love for China he threw himself into the West's effort to revive foreign influence and bring about his own advancement. He made a fashionable, expedient marriage. He strained every energy toward a high position and luxury. Seeking to identify himself completely with the West, he told himself he was maintaining the detachment toward China his mother had advocated. When the government had come back from Chungking, again he had been indifferent. And yet he had based all his dealings with the Chinese on their concept of friendship and right conduct. What had it led to? Imprisonment! What business was it of Mu San's how he had lived during those years?

"Leave me alone. Get out!" he shouted.

Mu San was elated. At last he had made the man angry.

When young Chen told Lo of David's anger, Lo was pleased. "I think he is ready now. You are to stay tomorrow night until you get his signature to the confession we have written for him to sign."

After Mu San left, David trod faster and faster the polished ring of boards, thinking of how to kill the man he hated. He'd pretend to be ready to sign the statement, continually thrust before him, then suddenly jump on Mu San and kill him with his bare hands.

The day broke. No morning meal was brought to him. At nine o'clock he heard the scampering feet of the kindergarten children quartered in the other half of the house. Their morning song—

> "Hate America,
> Love Mao Tse-tung,
> Love Science,
> Love the State."

Afternoon came, no afternoon meal. The children on their way home scampered across the veranda singing, "Hate America, hate—"

Darkness came, David sat on the edge of the cot, lips

tightly shut, waiting, waiting for his inquisitor, unmindful of the taunting voices of lesser adversaries.

Midnight, and Mu San came—he too obsessed with hatred, but confident now of his success.

"Tell me about what went on in the city in the twenty years you lived in Shanghai. Was not the social revolution destroyed here?"

"What had that to do with me?" cried David.

"Think what it had to do with you."

Now Mu San spoke not alone the words Lo had given him. He spoke out of his own hatred. Tight-lipped, he drove home his advantage, sensing his victim's armor was growing thin. He'd break the man's spirit!

"Would you like to be told the details of those years leading up to your work as a spy? You tremble. You don't wish to hear? What kind of friendship did you offer when China was hard beset by Japan?"

"I—I don't remember."

Again and again and again the questions, "How did you live during the last years you were in China? What did you, who profess such love for China, do to help bring about a stable government? After Chiang Kai-shek's government returned from Chungking and inflation set in you were ready to welcome any regime that would make you prosperous. When you saw things were getting hot for the Westerners you got out of China. You left a substitute to bear the hate you had helped to create. Then you came back and asked my father to risk my life to get out your substitute because you had once lent the family money—money," he reiterated in scorn.

"Surely it was not up to me to tell you how to manage your government." David tried thus to fend off the guilt beginning to press in on him—a load of guilt. Guilt of the West against the East, confused with his own guilt—his twenty years in Shanghai which had brought him material advancement and spiritual shrinkage, which had led to his betrayal of Paul Damon, guilt so heavy that David sagged under its weight. Let him crawl on his hands and knees to the feet of his hated accuser and confess for himself and his country.

"Confess you came back to destroy Shanghai."

Then he thought he heard his father's voice. "We have taken, but we have given. Both sides have made mistakes." David straightened his shoulders.

"Why did you come to spy? Who paid you?"

"I did not come to spy. I came to rescue an innocent man."

"You shall confess," screamed Mu San. "If you don't confess, I'll see you're punished here in this room. Die here as your substitute died. Confess! Sign this paper!" And Mu San thrust into David's trembling hands the written statement. "Read it."

It read: "I came to destroy by order of my government the waterworks and electric plant." Slowly David let the paper fall.

"Pick it up," shouted Mu San.

David did not move.

A new voice. "We are the secret police. You are both under arrest."

274

Two men jerked Mu San to his feet, tied his hands. One came over to David, put a pistol to his back.

"March," he commanded. "We've got to get on with this business."

Walking before him, David prayed that he would not yield under torture. Thus he would be absolved of the death of Paul Damon. He stumbled.

"Watch your step," commanded his guardian.

As he walked down the steps of his house, David thought he heard his name spoken, "Shao Con."

The streets were dark and empty. Pushed from behind, he quickened his pace . . . he was beginning to give out. The months of imprisonment had left him soft, his legs were swollen from the unrelieved diet of rice. But he must not give out, must not appear weak before his enemies. If only they'd reach their destination, however terrible that destination might prove to be.

They were in the Chinese countryside. A narrow, stone-flagged path and the croaking of the frogs told him so. Suddenly he was forced down the embankment. Again he stumbled. Instinctively he reached out his hands to steady himself. He touched the smooth bole of a tree—bamboo, he knew it by its smoothness.

Voices came from shadowy figures gathering round him. "You have him. Good!" It was a woman's voice. David knew the women were among the most cold and unfeeling of the Communists.

"And the other?"

"Yes, he is here too."

"Honorable Conway, we are guerrillas." It was an old

man's voice that uttered the words. "We are to be given arms by your friend, the Honorable Chen of Hong Kong, if we bring you back safely so that the Honorable Chen may fulfill his obligation to you. And the other, this despicable son of the honorable Chen, must be brought back to his father for punishment. His crime is great. Because of him you have been imprisoned. Third Uncle is dead. The head of the family, he who has the power of life and death over its members, will decide what his punishment shall be. Such is the custom in his land of the Hans. We must deliver you both or we do not receive arms. You will obey us explicitly."

Suddenly David felt the sweetness of the night air, the sweetness of freedom, the sweetness of having resisted to the end. Then he felt gratitude to these men who had saved him from the test of torture.

Chapter 21

CONFIDENTLY LO WAITED FOR
Mu San to come with David's signed confession. The
man evidently was all but broken, but he was stubborn.
Surely by morning the evidence of the American's crime
would be in Lo's hands. He would carry it to the tribunal.
He would be vindicated even in the eyes of the woman
who smiled at him so enigmatically. In a few hours the
Peking radio would be blaring forth the story of how a
prominent American had confessed that his country had
sent him to China to destroy her industrial equipment,
hold her to the status of a second-rate country. The world
would know, and each tiny village in China would know.

Men and women would tell it to the people in song and drama; the children would sing of it in their schools. This would be Lo's gift to the great father of the revolution, Mao Tse-tung. And it would free Lo forever from suspicion.

He lighted cigarette after cigarette, eager to the point of impatience for the moment to come when he would have the banker's confession. Earlier in the evening he had stood outside the foreigner's house for the purpose of watching the effect his questions, carefully planned for this last interrogation, were having upon the American. From much experience Lo was able to judge when a person's will was about to break. The face of the prisoner—unshaven, haggard; his tormented eyes seemed burned upon the darkness of the night. They were the eyes of an old friend—no! no! an enemy! Forget, forget those eyes!

Trying for the iron discipline which for years he had demanded of himself, Lo went over in his mind the lives of the men who had made the Long March across China to save the Communist Party; years when Chiang Kai-shek's troops had so ruthlessly pursued them. Those marching thousands, those ragged starving thousands who, under Mao's leadership, had crossed rivers and high mountain ranges on the way to a mountain stronghold to preserve the Communist dream. One of these men now headed Shanghai's governing committee. Often at meetings he was racked with fits of coughing from tuberculosis contracted during the Long March. Later he had gone to Moscow. There he had been trained in Marxist doctrine—such understanding of the absolutism of Marxism as Lo longed for, but in his humility felt he had not yet acquired. "Comrade," Lo murmured, "my comrade, you are a man completely divorced from any feeling for friends, province, village, family. Only the State matters to you—and to me."

All at once Lo had a sudden clear picture of his mother as he had seen her last—imperious mouth, brilliant, angry eyes. His mother would die, if necessary, to preserve the unending stream of the family that led back into the past and on into the future which the Party meant to destroy. A new order was soon to go out that at all costs the patriarchal families must be destroyed. And Lo's son? Would he be one to die fighting to preserve the family? Forget the family. A good Communist did not have such thoughts.

Too long had he waited for Mu San. He walked to the door, opened it. Day was breaking. No one coming. He closed the door, paced the room. Still Mu San did not come, and Lo, exhausted with hours of suspense, sank down by his bare table, put his head on his hands.

In a moment he started up. He must have been dreaming, but he could not shake off the dream figures. More vividly than if he stood there in flesh and blood Lo could see the man, John Conway, his eyes so like those of the prisoner. A tall, ungainly man—Da Con, they called him in Chinese —who after his son had left for America had taken Lo into his home. Evenings, when Lo returned from the meetings of a secret Communist cell, he would pause in the courtyard and if, through the pane of glass set into the center of the paper-paned window of the man's study, he saw him bent over his books, Lo would knock and the teacher would rise and open the door and the two would sit together.

Bits of their conversation were flung to the surface of Lo's mind—how the ancient and complex culture of the Chinese people might be brought into union with the young, aggressive West; how the beauties and excesses of each could be reconciled, brought into harmony. On such nights the two ways had battled within Lo—evolution or revolution.

He had chosen revolution. Once more he went over to the door and opened it. He could hear the songs of the New China coming to him from the teams of workers going out over the city to work—revolution! Let Mu San come with the American's confession. Once more he closed the door.

There was a knock, but not Mu San's timid knock. A pounding. Lo flung open the door. There, advancing toward him, were members of the secret police to which he belonged. "So you let the foreigner and your accomplice escape? Where are they?" demanded the head of the group.

"Escape!"

In that moment Lo recognized his defeat.

Handcuffs were put over Lo's slender wrists by his own comrades. On his own soft flesh he felt the iron that should have been circling the wrists of the foreigner. It was all clear to him now. From the first the foreigner, once his friend, and the young man, once his pupil, had plotted to destroy him. If he could just get his long fingers on Mu San's throat!

Lo stood facing his judges, among them the veteran of the Long March, the man he admired above all others, and the smiling woman, a flower in her hair this morning.

280

"So you, you of all men are a counterrevolutionary. You planned the prisoner's escape and you plotted with the capitalist youth who once was your student." The old man spoke sternly.

"I have been faithful to the State," cried Lo. "I know nothing of their escape." He raised his eyes from his accuser to the portrait of Mao Tse-tung, the father of the revolution. Suddenly the enormity of his own guilt was revealed to him—in his thoughts he had been unfaithful to the State.

"I am guilty," he cried.

"Tell us where they are, how they escaped," the old man of the tribunal demanded.

"I do not know."

"We have ways, as you know, to make you tell."

Lo was far beyond their reach now. Through the vicarious participation in the pain of others he had sought the rapture of mystical union with men—a mystical rapture he experienced only partially when he inflicted pain on others. Now he would be beaten, broken. For collective man he would die, so find mystical union with man, the deity, the Godhead.

Chapter 22

IN THE BAMBOO GROVE SUR-
rounded by his rescuers David leaned against the bole of a
tree. Now that there was no longer any need to steel himself against hatred, he was unable to rally enough strength
to meet kindness. "Drink," someone commanded, and he
took the bottle thrust into his hand, gratefully gulping
down the lukewarm tea. "Eat," came a second command
and he ate the lump of cold rice given him. "The honorable
one must have strength. Time cannot be allowed for rest."

Honorable one? Respect accorded to him!

"The guards are awake by now. The old woman didn't
have much opium. The sons of turtles will be after us. Even

the countryside will soon be alive with police and cadre. Each of you know what you're to do, my children. All our lives depend on everyone obeying my orders."

The voice that spoke these words was an old man's voice and untutored. And now that voice spoke to David. "You, honorable one, must also obey. Come with me." A strong hand grasped David's. Together they climbed the embankment that led to the road.

Often his companion, walking ahead of David, paused and listened. A half hour along dyke paths, a whisper in the dark, "Slide down into the paddy after me. Step carefully. Do not make a splashing sound in the paddy water." David lowered one foot, then the other into the water-soaked earth. Soon they came to a burial mound rising out of the paddy. "I hide you here. The owner hasn't yet obeyed the command to move his ancestors. He thinks it safe to defy the new government a little while longer. The government will be too busy today hunting you to make this man disturb his ancestors." The man moved a piece of sod and then some wires woven together. "In here, master." Next to the heavy planks of an ancient coffin a place had been cleverly hollowed out. David hesitated an instant, then crawled in. A whisper from his guide. "This humble one is pressing the sod carefully in place over the wire. Stay until I come."

The spring planting had begun, and when daylight came David could hear someone wading in the water-covered field. Two—a man and woman by their voices. He surmised they were transplanting green rice shoots from a seedbed. As little by little they came nearer to his hiding place, David was in panic! They would discover the loose sod and take him prisoner. No! They were friends. He would cry out, beg to be freed from his prison. No! No! Not only his own life, but that of the guerrillas who had risked their lives to rescue him depended on his silence. But as the interminable hours went by, he was all but overcome by fright. Suppose the old man, his guide, never did return? Suppose he was captured during the day? Better for David to free himself now. But by so doing he would put in jeopardy the life of the peasant in whose field he was hidden. So many risking their lives for him. He thought of the little jockey and his futile death. He thought of his old amah. Could it have been she who had drugged the guard? If so, could she possibly escape capture? No more lives must be offered for his. "Lie quiet," he spoke sternly to his cramped body. "Lie quiet," he spoke sternly to the spirit within. "This can be your victory." Finally he slept. The happenings of the past days rose to torment him. He woke in a cold sweat. He shivered. More hours.

And then a whisper, "I am here." The sod was lifted, oh, so quietly. The night air rushed in. "There is little food. We must get far tonight. One of ours has been captured. He may not be able to hold out against torture." The torture which had been intended for David was being inflicted on one of his rescuers. Still another life offered for his. As David followed the man out of the paddy, he marshalled all his strength to meet the demands of the march.

Hungry, thirsty, sometimes barely escaping capture, they worked their way across the plain that lay between them and the comparative safety of the mountains. David lost count of the nights and the days: nights when he stumbled after his guide, his swollen legs often buckling under him, waded through paddies supported by a man he never saw clearly; days when he accepted living burial under rubbish, in grave mounds, behind coffins of ancestors stacked in pavilions awaiting the government's edict as to their disposal.

But finally a time came when his companion seemed unconcerned that light penetrated the bamboo grove they entered. The old peasant, for such David now saw his companion was, cut one of the bamboo shoots sprung up during the night, and gave it to David to chew. "Its moisture will help you." The words were not whispered. In the misty green light of the grove, David, lightheaded from lack of food, felt as if he moved forward under water. Then the waters parted and they stood in the open on a path which brought them to a pavilion erected in ancient times to shelter tired wayfarers. Tall trees surrounded it. David's head cleared. He knew where he was. Often during his years in Shanghai when out hunting he had rested in this quiet spot. How welcome now the play of shadow and light among the trees after the long months in the glare of an uncovered electric light, and the days since his rescue when he had lain in dark graves, still as in death, and nights when he and his escort had prowled toward the day which they feared to have come.

"This is Buddhist ground not yet taken over by the government, but the priests are not here. Those among them who will testify for the State live in comfort in the cities, those who are stubborn have been put to work build-

ing a railroad far away. The people fear to come here."
After a while the peasant rose. "We start now," he said.
"By night we must be at our hiding place." He raised his
eyes to the denuded hills of China from which the trees had
long ago been cut for firewood. They offered little shelter.

It was slow going. The hills that looked smooth in the
distance were a mass of jagged ends—the cutoff branches
of shrubs bruised the men's ankles; azaleas, thwarted in
their growth by the sickles of the peasants, had sent their
shoots along the ground, often tripping them. Once, twice,
David fell. His breath came in short gasps. Always his
guide urged him on.

At last at dusk they came to some shallow stone steps.
Helped by his guide, David made the ascent, stepped onto
a great paved court. Beyond was the open door of a temple.
Within David could dimly see a golden Buddha seated on
golden lotus leaves. But no incense burned in the great incense burner, no priests came out to welcome them or beg
alms.

"O Mi To Vet, O Mi To Vet, to the holy Buddha, to
the holy Buddha," the old man murmured as he placed the
palms of his hands together and bowed to the golden image
within the temple. Then he turned away cursing the new
government.

Again they climbed, and now they came to a grove of
scrub pines. The low-growing branches scraped across
their faces. "Almost there, master."

"Almost." A term David had heard since childhood—
spoken by a Chinese it might mean anything—a few yards,
a mile. A li, the measurement in China, was one length in

hilly country, another in flat country. His long confinement, his lack of sleep, had lessened his resistance. He wavered. He felt the old peasant's hand under his elbow. "A little farther, master," he coaxed.

Again a courtyard and smooth stones were under David's feet. "Halt!" a voice out of the darkness. An answer from the peasant—a password undoubtedly—for unhindered they now moved forward. A hooded lamp above a doorway gave forth enough light for David to see that this was one of the temple's outbuildings where guests were housed when they came to pray or to seek retreat. Evidently even the most zealous Communist had not dared as yet to invade this place. Otherwise it would not be the hideout for the guerrillas. His escort led David toward the door with the lamp over it, and said to some unseen person, "We have arrived."

A bamboo screen was lifted from the doorway, revealing a dimly lighted room and a figure which at first David took to be that of a man, but as they drew nearer he saw to his amazement that he faced the young girl who had taken part in the previous attempt to rescue him. He sank down on the stool inside the doorway. He closed his eyes. A cup was pressed against his lips. He smelled the sweet odor of rice wine. "You must drink it." Gently the words were spoken. He felt warm liquid in his mouth. With an effort he swallowed.

Revived, he looked around. Some kind of court proceedings seemed to be going on. Three men sat behind a table at the end of the room. The old peasant, his escort, sat between the other two! A slight youth knelt before them, his head touching the floor. Men with rifles stood at attention, one on each side of the half-prostrate man.

"Come," said the girl, who had given him the wine. She led David to a spot in front of the prisoner, who was now jerked to his feet. It was Mu San! Mu San, who stared at him in sullen anger!

The leader of the band, the ragged, unkempt old man who had brought David safely across the plain, spoke. "Under orders of your father, Chen Mu San, we captured both you and this foreigner. By the ancient custom of China it is necessary that your honorable father's friend should be returned safely from his journey undertaken under your protection. This we shall endeavor to do. In your father's house in Hong Kong he will be welcomed and given the honors a friend should receive. During the journey, he is our guest. As for you, dog that you are, you are a prisoner to be delivered over to your father to receive punishment for your crime against your father's friend and your ancestors—Third Uncle is dead. The graves of your ancestors have been destroyed."

Mu San stared defiantly at his judges. "I have committed no crime. My father is the State. I have obeyed my father. You and this despicable foreigner are the ones who have betrayed China." He spoke proudly.

The guards moved a step nearer. "Silence," sternly the old man commanded the prisoner. "If we had our way, we would punish you now, but we are under command of your father to leave that for him. But if you seek to escape you will be shot. The foreigner, as soon as he recovers from the treatment he has received at your hands, will guard you

288

on the march. He will guard you well. Hate is a good watchman with revenge for a partner."

Now the two were led from the council room, taken to separate quiet cubicles—Mu San to be guarded, David to be ministered to.

Angrily the young Chinese told himself he would escape when the guerrilla outside his door fell asleep. He knew these hills. Each year of his childhood he and his family had been housed for a few days in these very rooms when the masses for the dead were held for the Chen ancestors. The men of Chen's family were not Buddhists, but they did not disparage the faith of the women in Buddha, deeming it well to reverence Buddha lest after all he be a god. His former dutiful attendance on Buddha, Mu San felt, would serve him well now, for those yearly pilgrimages had given him knowledge he needed to make his escape. When the guard slept he would quietly lift the small window at the back of the room, crawl through, and follow the paths which led to a village on the other side of the mountain.

But where would he go? There was no mercy in the lexicon of the Communists for failure such as his. Once he had been given clemency for letting the foreigner slip out of his hands; clemency for the same offense would not be given a second time. They would not even believe his story. They would consider him a traitor. No, he was forever cast out from the New China. He could not go back.

But to go forward with these guerrillas was also a disaster. He could expect no leniency from his father when he was delivered to him. According to the ancient law, a father had the power of life and death over a son—and his father lived by the ancient law. His offense was not only against his father, but against his father's father, back, back into antiquity, the enormity of his offense increasing in ratio as the generations behind him increased. Nothing was left him—nothing except to take revenge on the man who had made him an outcast. He'd wait his time to kill the American who had robbed him of his entrance into the white-hot core of communism.

Finally he slept. He dreamed he was a little boy come to serve the dead. Kneeling on a soft mat, the palms of his hands pressed together, he watched the monks' flickering fingers portraying man given over, because of his brutality, to endless migrations, coming back again and again to pain on the wheel of life.

Far into the next day David slept, ministered to even in sleep although he was not conscious of it. At last he woke, looked around, started up, looked again. Surely the man who squatted on the floor at his side was not—yes, it was! No, it couldn't be! "Te Lin, is it really you?"

"None other. Once a tender of ponies, now a guerrilla," Te Lin chuckled.

"But, Te Lin, you were killed."

"Yes, killed, but I return to serve you." Again he chuckled.

"How?"

"We guerrillas do not talk of our ways of escape. And now master would bathe?"

As he rose and left the room David realized, despite the

290

chuckles, the old Te Lin was gone. This Te Lin was toughened and hardened and proud as he had never been before. Soon Te Lin entered with warm water, soap, a towel, and even a native razor. Slowly David soaped himself, washed, soaped himself again, washed, finally poured the last of the clean water over him. The razor was dull, but he managed to shave with it. At last cleansed of the taint of his imprisonment he sat down on the rude bed, the only article of furniture in the room.

Almost immediately Te Lin entered with a steaming hot bowl of vegetables. There was also a tangerine and, to David's astonishment, a can of American tomato juice! From where could it have come? Every pore of David's body seemed to reach out for the tangerine and the tomato juice, but he managed to offer to share them with his friend. Te Lin, squatting on the floor beside him, refused although his eyes surveyed these delicacies hungrily. "Luxury softens a man, and I am a man such as I have never been before. As for you, you must become strong," he said.

After the meal David slept again, content as a child to be cared for. But his next awakening was different. His mind began to function. He was a member of a hunted band. He must not be more of a burden than necessary on these guerrillas, desperately trying to survive. Even if they had not been hunted before, they would certainly be ruthlessly hunted now. One of them had already been captured. Were there any more who had been sacrificed for him? Then his mind veered. Had there been an old woman who had helped in his escape? If so, who was she? Was there any chance of rescuing her? He raised himself on his elbow and asked these questions of Te Lin faithfully squatting by his side.

"My humble self does not know. Each does his part." Te Lin's words carried a quiet rebuke unheeded by David. "By any chance was the old woman my former amah?" he insisted. Te Lin shook his head. "I do not know, better talk to the girl."

When later she came in, David explained, "I asked, hoping that somehow the old woman could be saved."

"Many die these days," she answered.

"Do you know who she was?"

"It is best not to ask questions. We have little opportunity to know what is happening. We are hunted people. It's much more desperate for us than it ever was for guerrillas during the Japanese occupation. Then they could get food from the people. None now dare offer us food. The amount of rice each peasant has harvested is known. A cupful would be missed. We must forage for vegetables, snare fish if possible from ponds, live on whatever we can steal."

"Could I ask you one more question? Do you know how my substitute, Paul Damon, died?"

"Obey, and not question is your part. In a few months, if we can fulfill our promises, you will be restored to your own people," she answered. "This much I can tell you: The plan is to follow the hills south until we come to a valley broken by bits of swamp; it leads into the delta of the Pearl River; that has always been pirates' country. If we can get hold of a sampan we stand a chance of getting over to the coast. Somehow we must get into Macao, where we can cast ourselves on the mercy of the colony."

An impossible plan, thought David, but any escape was always impossible and yet people *had* escaped.

This girl was intelligent. She seemed to think escape was possible, but who was she? Why should this high-born girl be a member of this band of guerrillas?

After her talk with David the girl returned to the task of helping Old Five divide between the men the necessary articles which they must have in what they hoped would be a quick march south. She urged that one small kettle be included in case they ever were lucky enough to get rice. They might even find a spot where they dared heat water and make a little tea. "What does a girl like you know of guerrilla life?" grumbled the old man. "But take your kettle."

They had a few quilts, but not enough to go around. Ammunition and rifles were given to the most reliable. Packages of cold rice were wrapped in oiled paper, one for each man. They would have to drink from the streams.

When the task was completed the girl sought a place where she could be alone. She found it finally—a niche behind the Goddess of Mercy in one of the small ante-rooms of the temple. Ever since David Conway and young Chen had been brought into camp she had found it difficult to maintain the aloof attitude which her father, when he put her under Old Five's care, had told her would be necessary. Her only chance not to be regarded in the eyes of the men as a camp follower would lie in this aloofness—"maintain it always," he had insisted. Old Five could be trusted. He would regard the care of the daughter of his former

293

landlord as a sacred trust. As tenant farmer, Old Five had done well. Furthermore the girl's father had helped him escape after the Communists took over.

When Old Five had brought her to the guerrillas' hiding place he had called her the girl, meaning, the maiden. Her name he never spoke, nor did she. And Old Five had made her his assistant, often sending her on difficult missions. Gradually she had become an heroic figure to the men. Aloof, unapproachable, she had steeled herself to living outside the boundaries of companionship, shut into her own grief over the death of her parents after the underground had been discovered. The short interview with David had made her long for human companionship. He stirred memories of happier days. Ever since she could remember, Americans and Englishmen had been in and out of the house of her father. Dating back to the Boxer rebellion her family had been interested in reform. Some of the men had been abroad for their education; her father was one of them. Her mother had early insisted on attending a foreign school. The girl had spoken English since she was a small child. In her conversation with David she had almost yielded to the desire to speak to him in his own language. But she had not.

But he had awakened memories which she could not still: of her life in Nanking—all that it meant to be the beloved, petted daughter of an official in the Nationalist government—a girl of seventeen sent to school each morning in her father's limousine, riding home in the late afternoon through the crowded streets, the crowds dispersing to let the car pass. She belonged to the younger set who above all else sought to be modern, especially free to fall in love as Westerners did and escape family discipline.

But soon her happiness had been clouded. There was the flight to Chungking and, on the government's return, her father, who had criticized men close to Chiang Kai-shek, had been accused by them of being a Communist and he had been imprisoned. She had been held as a witness against him. Her mutilated right hand testified to the fact of her loyalty to her father.

When the Communists took over, her father had been freed but he had joined the underground and had been captured when the underground was discovered. Before his capture, knowing that it was inevitable, he had sent her to Lao Wu although she had pleaded to die with him. "It is according to our ancient custom," she had reminded him. "My mother will not leave you. Why should I?"

"It is different with your mother," he had insisted. "Obey me." Such a hard task he had set her; easier to die than to live among these rough men.

But now she felt comforted thinking of the foreigner. She could not avail herself of his companionship but he was among them.

Chapter 23

ON THE THIRD NIGHT, DAVID was awakened by an unusual amount of coming and going outside. He arose and looked out. Men, by twos and threes, were stealthily leaving the courtyard. Each carried a small bundle, some larger ones. Were they deserting him? Then Te Lin, carrying a larger bundle, came into the room. "We've got to get out of here. The man they captured has betrayed us," he said and added, "this bundle holds what the two of us need." And David was ashamed that he had lost his capacity to believe in these men who had already risked their lives to save him. Quickly he put on the clean, but worn clothes and cloth-soled sandals Te Lin

296

handed him. Then together they went out into the court, where David was given a pistol and ammunition and Te Lin a rifle. "Guard it well," commanded the old peasant, the leader. "We have only a little ammunition."

Guard it, I certainly will, thought David. I shall never let myself be taken alive.

As they came into the main temple, he saw Mu San walking between two men toward the outer door. David sprang forward. The little jockey pulled at his sleeve. "You are not strong enough yet. When your strength comes back the traitor will be put in your care, but remember, only if both of you live will you get your freedom."

The first ten nights were a desperate flight from their pursuers. They dared not descend to the inhabited valleys. Obscured by the darkness they followed the mountain ridges up one peak, along the mountain saddle, up another peak. For David, these marches brought acute suffering. His muscles, weakened by long disuse, were flabby; often he had to lean on the little jockey who was his constant attendant. The days were scarcely less difficult when he lay with the others hidden in the low growth of the mountainside with little to eat or drink. The sun beat down from a mercilessly clear sky and the insects and mosquitoes swarmed around him and the other sweaty men.

He soon realized that he, representative of the country fighting their sons in Korea, was rejected as much by these guerrillas as Mu San was, the only difference being that he was treated with a studied respect while Mu San was reviled and despised. Both were a burden on the guerrillas in their grim struggle to survive. But there was always Te Lin, his faithful friend.

Bit by bit, from chance remarks the men made to each other as they lay in the scrub, David learned about this band of outlaws on whom his life depended. Its core was made up of the remnants of an organization of peasants who had operated as guerrillas during the Japanese invasion. They had gone back to their farms when the Japanese were defeated, but after the Communists took over, for one reason or another, they had again taken to the hills. Their leader, Lao Wu, Old Five, was one of these. But it was not the old man's choosing that he should continue his guerrilla activities. A peasant at heart, he loved the soil on which his ancestors had lived and he had wished, after the war was over, to be left in peace to till his land. But his son, who had faithfully tended the rice paddies during the Japanese war while his father was away, had all the time been a secret member of the Communist Party, and when the Communists took over the country he had denounced his father, informing the authorities that the old man had arms hidden. Lao Wu's son, his only son, had disclosed the hiding place of one rifle and a little ammunition kept to protect the family in time of need! Old Five had had to flee for his life.

The girl was the daughter of an official originally in the Nationalist regime who, when the Communists came in, had helped to organize the underground. After its exposure by Mu San, the father had been captured, but he had succeeded in getting his daughter to Lao Wu, once one of his tenants.

Te Lin had been brought to the band by the girl who had somehow rescued him the night David was captured. The details of that rescue Te Lin would not divulge. He continued to insist, "Te Lin does not give away secrets of rescue."

The rest of the group consisted of a petty merchant, several rich peasants who had been denounced by poorer peasants, and two men who during the Japanese invasion had become guerrillas and now did not wish to relinquish the marauder's way of life. Tiger One Eye and Tiger Two Eyes, as they were called, had been the ones to make the contact with Chen Senior in Hong Kong. This gave them, or so they seemed to think, special privileges.

This heterogeneous group, David soon realized, was held together by some power Lao Wu wielded over them. They grumbled about the distribution of the meager rations and, rough men as most of them were, they quarreled between themselves as to who should possess the girl if the chance was given them. But Old Five held them in restraint. He had taken the responsibility for the daughter of the man he formerly served. "According to our custom trust must be respected," he told them. "She has been put in my care by her father, who has died because he sought to defy the wicked men who have taken over our homes. Thus she becomes your responsibility, too." There was a sturdy integrity in the old man which even the roughest among them respected. Lao Wu was a keeper of dauli, the custom. He was ding hao, "good," and they obeyed him.

With the ruthless efficiency it had displayed in all reforms, the new government was attempting to exterminate all guerrillas, and there was no trick known in guerrilla warfare—foraging for food, or seeking out clever hiding places—not known to the government. Mao Tse-tung, the Great Father, a guerrilla himself during the years when Chiang Kai-shek had relentlessly pursued him, had written a manual on guerrilla warfare. It was required reading by militia, police, cadres, and even villagers.

At the end of two months, due to the detours they had been obliged to make to escape capture, the band was only a bare hundred miles south of the spot from which they had started. And as these higher ranges lay farther inland they were farther from the coast than in the beginning.

They had to venture down into the narrow valleys to get food—vegetables, a handful here, a handful there, jerked out of peasants' fields. While so doing, two of their number had been shot. The foraging had to take place during the night marches. Lao Wu divided the men into groups of two or three. Once all had learned the meeting place for the next day, cave or hillside, the band separated. More and more the girl took the lead in these foraging expeditions. She was brave and she was clever. The only ones who did not forage but took a direct course to the meeting place were Mu San, David and one guerrilla who knew the hills well enough to bring them to their destination.

During the march Mu San went unhandcuffed; handcuffed he would have found walking over rough ground all but impossible. A rope, which David held, was tied around Mu San's waist. In the other hand David held his revolver. Grimly he performed his duty as guard, alert to the possibility that Mu San might make a break for freedom, and freedom David intended should never be granted to this traitor. Punishment meted out to Mu San by his father was all that now concerned David, his own sense of guilt over the death of Damon swallowed up in his hatred for the young Chinese who had kept him from the atonement he longed to make to Paul Damon. But sometimes, during the long hours of the day when he lay hidden on a hillside, for a brief moment a sense of harmony would be his as he looked down at the green valley below with its ordered rice fields and across to the undulating hills opposite, shadows lying softly in the hollows; he, as in his childhood, became one of the ten thousand harmonious things of the universe. Then rain drenching his thin coat or sun burning his skin, blinding him with its brilliant heat, would make the universe into another enemy, only to have his hostilities pierced with wonderment over Te Lin's devotion to him.

Chapter 24

IT WAS A HOT, STEAMY MORN-
ing. There had been rain in the night, and the sun now at
noon shining through the moisture-laden air seemed more
intolerable than bright sunlight to the little band lying flat
in the scrub on the saddle between two hills—the rendez-
vous agreed upon for the day. There had been an especially
daring foraging expedition the night before because of the
band's desperate need of food. Three had not returned. No
one knew whether they had been shot, captured, or just
delayed. Te Lin was one of them. They had no fear he
would divulge the fact that he was a member of the guerrilla group which held David and Mu San, the two so

sought after by the government, but Little Mouse, so nicknamed for his timidity, who had not returned, they feared would tell all under torture. If so, the band would have to abandon its course south and go west into rougher mountain country, but if Little Mouse had been killed outright they would feel safe in continuing their direct route south. Their revered leader, Lao Wu, was the third one missing. Whatever happened to him, he would remain faithful, but no one really believed that he had been caught. His prowess was great. He was an old and an experienced guerrilla. He surely would soon be among them.

But gradually they grew fearful that he had been caught and they began to discuss what to do. David, lying a little apart, trying to work out in his own mind what would happen if Lao Wu was not here to control the others, listened as best he could to the talk. He heard the girl say, "Let me go down into the valley and learn what has happened. I can slip in among the villagers, I will sing the songs of the revolution. I'll say I'm a member of a cadre sent over from another village. I'll try to find out what has happened. Even if Little Mouse has given us away, they will not think to ask him if there is a woman among the guerrillas he belonged to." David was stirred out of himself by admiration for the girl's bravery. But how foolhardy! It would only mean that she, too, would be lost, the best brains of the outfit. But knowing his advice would not be welcome, he kept still.

"Let her go, a woman is less needed than a man," said one of the Tigers.

"Yes, less needed than a man," all agreed.

The girl started to crawl away through the grass when David, unable to remain out of the council longer, pointed out where the ammunition belt which she usually carried slung over her shoulder had left its mark on her jacket. "They'll know you're not a member of a cadre." He hoped thus to save her, at least till Lao Wu returned—desperately he hoped for Lao Wu's return.

"You are clever, like our own people," said one of the guerrillas, turning to David, admiration in his voice.

"But who has a jacket not so marked? Do you think we are rich with garments for every occasion?" another asked scornfully.

"Would you have her go without a jacket?" asked Tiger One Eye as he grinned licentiously. His loose heavy mouth hung open, showing his stained and rotten teeth.

"There is one among us who has no mark on his jacket. The prisoner, Mu San, has not carried arms. His jacket is not marked," said David.

"Well spoken," they all cried. Roughly they stripped Mu San of his top garment. For this moment, David was one of them.

The girl knelt in their midst and addressed them all. "You will hand me the coat and I will go a little apart from you while I change, and I will then go to the valley as your scout. And you are to stay here until my return. If Lao Wu comes, you are to tell him where I have gone and why. If neither of us returns by night, you will go to the next hiding place and await us there. Give me your promise." And to the girl in ragged trousers and short jacket with a man's visor cap perched on her untidy hair, some willingly, some unwillingly gave the promise she asked.

Taking Mu San's coat, she crawled to the other slope of the saddle. When she returned, she handed her own coat to the prisoner, saying, "Put it on, wear it until my return." And without looking at the others, she crawled away through the scrub.

It was a long anxious afternoon for them all—waiting for Old Five to appear, waiting for the girl to return, waiting for Te Lin, waiting for Little Mouse. In the low scrub in the hollowed saddle between the two mountains they lay, first in the shadow of one mountain, then in the shadow of the other as the sun moved westward. Stationing an outpost to warn them if a peasant by chance should come up from the valley, they slept. David feigned sleep. By lying very still he could catch bits of whispered conversation going on between the two Tigers. "If Old Five doesn't come back, we should strike out for ourselves. Take old Chen's son, collect the money promised us."

"It's no good," argued another, "if we don't bring in the foreign devil. Take them both."

There arose in David a determination to outwit these two who, in absence of Old Five, cravenly plotted against him. Although the band did not accept him, David now identified himself with them. While in prison, he had come to feel that he was shut out from society. Rescued by these outlaws, he had been grateful to them, grateful to Te Lin for his friendship but he had locked himself away fearful to stir outside the confines of himself. Now he would offer loyalty to the band.

Mu San, who had earlier been shackled and placed a little apart from the others, was watching the two men whispering together. He had long ago known they were bad men and he guessed what they were planning to do, but it meant nothing to him whether they or the band held him. In either case he was the prisoner to be delivered to his father for punishment; in either case tied to the foreigner with an invisible thong, stronger than any leather one. In dumb despair Mu San went over the events of the night when he had all but brought this American to confess his betrayal of China. That confession was to have been Mu San's gift to the New China from which he was now forever shut out. The fatalism, long a part of the history of his people, took over. "Mei yu fat su—there is no way out."

Restlessly the men turned and twisted, slapped off the mosquitoes. Someone crawled in among them. "I have returned." It was Te Lin, spent from his slow crawl through the scrub. His face was scratched by the underbrush, his clothes were torn, but he clutched a few wilted vegetables. "We were chased out of a field. I do not know where the others are." No use asking him more. He slept, snoring and groaning in his sleep.

Shadows were settling over their hiding place. The outpost who had been stationed near a path leading up from the village signaled. "Someone is crawling through the brush."

"The girl?"

"Too far away to see."

Someone from the village who would betray their hiding place?

306

"Wait until the last moment to fire." Those were Lao Wu's instructions. There was no ammunition to waste.

A man crawled out on the path. The guard nervously fingering the trigger of his rifle suddenly shot—just in time, he believed, to save the girl for he could hear her singing the Communist song she had told them she would sing, a pause between the lines, as if for breath. No one else sang the song like that. It was her signal.

As she reached the fallen man her song died away. "Stupid one," she cried to the guard. "How could you fail to know Lao Wu? What have you done?"

Carefully they carried Lao Wu from the path. They bent over him, opened his jacket. In the failing light peered at the deep wound in his chest. They had no drugs, no surgical instruments, no doctor to help them. Vainly they tried to stanch the flow of blood beginning to fill his lungs.

Old Five opened his eyes and struggled to speak. "Little children, I have been your father. There is none among you to take that place. The cleverest of you must be your leader." His eyes travelled over the motley group gathered around him and came to rest on the girl kneeling by his side. "This one I make your leader . . . Swear you will obey her, my children." There was a moment of hesitation. Then each in turn made his vow.

"Swear you will deliver the prisoner and the foreigner to the honorable Chen. And the man who knows best the mountains I appoint to choose each day's hiding place." Lao Wu pointed to the man who had shot him. "He is to decide . . . each night's march. Swear—"

They swore.

A great bird of prey flew low overhead. Even without the sound of the swooping wings, all were too well acquainted with death not to know that Old Five was dead.

The girl spoke. "They captured Little Mouse. He betrayed us under torture. The villagers are frightened that they will be punished because of us. As leader I give my first order—we do not stop to bury the honorable Lao Wu. We must go now, we cannot wait longer. We will all march together tonight. No one is to forage." She turned to the man who had killed Lao Wu. "Lead the way," she commanded.

"Trigger," as they immediately named him in derision for stupidly killing Old Five, led them over the saddle, down the other side of the mountain away from the village where Little Mouse had been captured. But as they came near another village some of the men stopped, unwilling to follow the man who had displayed so little judgment before and was now leading them into a new danger by taking them so near to human habitations.

"There must be no dissent. Follow the guide without question. Only in unity can we survive," commanded the girl.

The path across the narrow valley barely skirted the single street of the town. Showing faintly in the twilight were the gray tiles of roofs, and beneath, the glimmer of white, plastered house walls. Over the roofs rose misty gray veils, signifying the evening meal was being cooked. Involuntarily the line of men paused. The girl spoke softly, "We must not falter." They moved off into the night—homesick, hungry, frightened.

For a week it seemed to David that allegiance to the girl hung in the balance. He knew that during its long history, in times of trouble, China had often produced strong women who, for one reason or another, had stepped out of the confining life of the partriarchal family to lead their men in revolt, even battle. But did this girl have such strength? Too, she was young. In their households, Chinese of all classes were accustomed to being ruled by their women, but complete power was not given to a woman until she was old. Then, as matriarch of the family, her rule became absolute. Would these guerrillas give complete obedience to this girl who must be somewhere in her twenties? David knew she would never gain the complete loyalty of the Tigers, but if the others remained loyal it would be enough.

David marvelled to see how one after the other, although often reluctantly, the men began to obey the girl. Alternately scolding and coaxing them, she trained them into a tight organization—something Lao Wu had never done. She set up rules and goals to be reached. She lengthened the night marches whenever possible. She no longer allowed the days to be spent in idleness. "Sleep first, my children," she would say, "later we weave sandals out of grass that you need not go barefoot." She had two needles and a little thread left in the sewing kit she had brought with her and she taught the men how to mend their clothes. So the little band, as summer progressed, moved steadily south. And to David's surprise even the Tigers seemingly were loyal to her. Evidently for the time being they realized it was better to yield to her.

But having overheard the Tigers' plotting on the afternoon of Lao Wu's death, David sought an opportunity to warn her not to trust them. But she, like the rest of the band, still treated him as an outsider. Then David, thinking he might reach her through Te Lin, whispered his doubts to Te Lin. Loud enough so the others could hear, the little jockey whispered back, "Let us gamble together. Gamble with grasses—a game I have invented. The Tigers will join us." During the long hours of the afternoon they played Te Lin's game and David was left to wonder whether there was any purpose in what Te Lin had proposed. Gambling to the little jockey appeared to be the cure-all in every emergency. Toward evening the girl, who had been asleep at a little distance, crawled over to the men to arrange for the night's march. When she saw that the men were neither sleeping nor busying themselves in making sandals, some gambling, others watching, all betting, she was irate as only a Chinese woman can be. She called upon the heavens to fall upon them. Their families were to lose their fertility. She scolded them until she was hoarse.

And the men, even the Tigers, surveyed their leader with real respect. David looking at Te Lin saw his eyes were full of admiration. "Ai yah," he murmured, "my old woman could not have done better." He chuckled.

Chapter 25

GRADUALLY THEIR NUMBERS were reduced: one died from malaria, several were shot and killed while pillaging the fields. None fortunately were captured. Then came the morning when Te Lin did not return. One of the Tigers reported that he had seen him shot down by an irate farmer.

David mourned for his friend. Had he by any chance by enlisting Te Lin's help in guarding the girl brought down upon his friend the enmity of these two lawless men in their midst? Had one of the Tigers shot Te Lin? If so he, David, again had been the instrument in destroying a friend.

The girl came and stretched out near him saying, "You, too, should learn to make sandals. None now in this small band can be spared from labor." Between her instructions she introduced words of comfort. "Friendship is a precious thing . . . The grass must be handled thus . . . You must be a good man to have produced such devotion as Te Lin gave you . . . No, you do not handle the grass correctly . . . Let me take his place as your friend . . . You have a Chinese name?" she asked.

"Yes, as a child I was called Shao Con. Con is my family's Chinese name. My father was called Da Con. He was always called the Big Con."

"My children, listen," she said in a louder whisper, "Shao Con is the name by which this honored one is to be known among us from now on."

"So it shall be," said the men. And David wondered anew at this inexhaustible fountain of friendship that existed in the Chinese—friendship offered him by this valiant girl who had now taken it upon herself to be his friend among men who considered him a man apart. He feared for her anew. But she seemed to lead a charmed life. She went unmolested into the fields, she even ventured sometimes to the edge of a village in order to pick up information about troop movements. One night, as she was pulling vegetables in a field, a man rose out of the patch. Quickly she snatched up her rifle from where it lay on the ground at her side.

"Don't shoot," he whispered, "I seek sanctuary. I offer you a little rice."

Accepting what he said as truth, she took him with her

to the day's hiding place. The rice was acceptable to the others, but not the man. Twice she brought such refugees back with her. No one openly opposed her, but when she brought in a third, even the most loyal peasant in the group protested. "You're like a hungry tiger. You leap on the bait, not waiting to see if there is a trap."

"You are safer than you have ever been," the man she had rescued explained. "I was once the magistrate in my village. I came to you, having heard the legend that is spreading from village to village about your leader."

"And what is the story?" the unbelieving guerrillas demanded.

"It is that a woman, small but powerful, supernaturally endowed, visits innumerable villages in one night to rescue peasants who are being searched out because they had resisted having their tools and their animals taken over by the cooperatives. The legend goes that anyone who refuses to obey the new edicts can invoke the presence of your supernaturally endowed leader. None will harm you as long as the people believe this legend."

The girl now pressed the men as never before, knowing it was advisable to get as far on their way as possible before the officials learned of the legend and hunted the band out more ruthlessly than ever until all of them were killed and the legend killed with them. In the meantime the legend was useful, for a little food was sometimes left where the girl could get it, and they were no longer shot at by the peasants.

Chapter 26

THEN CAME A NIGHT WHEN the legend must be proved or abandoned. A child rose from the field where the girl was and whispered, "A woman, a teacher in the next village is to be tried for wrong thoughts. Will the legendary woman rescue her?"

An overwhelming desire came over the girl to make this rescue—have another woman in the band and, against the judgment of most of the band, she decided to make the attempt. At dusk of the following day there was the usual subdued bustle of their forthcoming departure. The girl was conferring with Trigger over the next day's gathering place. Now she set about dividing the men into groups. All were to take as straight a course as possible to the meeting place, except the magistrate whom she had recently made a member of the band and Tiger One Eye. Those two were to go with her to rescue the teacher. Tiger Two Eyes was to accompany David and Mu San. Naive as the girl might seem in trusting the sincerity of the child of the night before who had asked her to do this dangerous thing, she was not as naive as David had thought her when it came to trusting the two Tigers. She always saw that they never marched in the same groups. When everything was arranged she sent two scouts to go down close to the villages and bring back word whether there were troops on the outskirts of the valley.

Halfway down the slope they heard a stirring in the brush. Suddenly a woman rose up at their side. When they reached for her, she made no effort to escape.

"Let your hearts be at rest, I come as a friend—I who know the ancient law of friendship. I want to speak to your leader. Let her come to me here."

When the word was brought to the girl by one of the scouts, she made no move to go. "If she is one of us, she will not fear to come among us. Bring her here," she commanded.

"Here! Right into our midst!" several exclaimed.

"Bring her here immediately," commanded the girl. "There can be but one leader. If command is divided, we perish."

There was no further protest, but the men hid their faces from the woman when she came among them. Even David took that precaution.

But the girl looked full into the face of the middle-aged woman. Her serenity and dignity indicated she had been trained from childhood in the tradition of womanly repose. Immediately the girl felt trust in her. "I am a teacher," the woman said, "and I teach for the Communists. This I want you to know."

"Why did you venture to come here?" asked the girl. "Did you think we would let you return?"

"Yes, because I come in order to warn you. Do not stop to rescue the woman you planned to tonight. It is a trap set to catch you and destroy the legend. Travel as fast as you can and don't go south, for that is the route they expect you to take."

"She is sent to trap us. Let us kill her and get on our way. Let us not leap on this bait." The oldest peasant among them spoke in warning, his words coming muffled from his jacket which he had drawn over his head and face.

"If you do not let me go, the whole countryside from now on will be against you," the woman answered. "I must hurry back before my absence is discovered. I warn you because I respect you. A leader such as yours preserves the wisdom of the past." She looked from the girl to Mu San, who had not hidden his face, and now she addressed her words to him. "We are an old people. Dynasties have come and gone, as you know. What are a few years in the life of a people thousands of years old? The river of life," she murmured. "Out of time it flows; into time it flows; just now it swirls in dark recesses. 'After the ebb, the flow.' So speaks our honored historian." Her voice sank to a whisper, then rose again to a tone of command, and she turned to the girl. "You have no time to waste. You as leader are a legend to the people at present. While that lasts, they will not betray you."

For a moment the girl did not answer, weighing the words of the experienced guerrilla that this might be a trap—reason and experience were both on his side. But intuition, wholly feminine, was speaking within her. This woman, as gently born as I, understands me, a voice within her said; I can trust her. There is a trap, but it is not the trap these men think it is. Those who would capture me let this woman leave the village and come here believing we would kill her. She is the woman we were to rescue to-night. If we kill her, the faith that the people have in me will be shattered. They will say I am no better than the Communists and in the future they will give us no protection. In anger they will betray us. Even if we take her with us to save her life, the story will be circulated that we killed her and none will know differently.

She looked into the eyes of the band of men she led, not certain that she would be able to free the woman against their united determination to kill her. But to free her was to deliver her to the Communists, who would kill her. Any way the girl looked lay death for the woman and possibly death for the band. Even if she followed the woman's instructions, there was no surety that the all-seeing eye of the Communists would not track them down. At last the girl spoke, "Go in peace and accept our gratitude." None of the guerrillas protested against their leader's decision, fearful of defying her. Through the years guerrillas who had often worked with women had come to believe that in times of danger a woman was endowed with a special faculty; in such times, one defied a woman's counsel at his own peril. No, they would not oppose the girl's decision.

The woman for a moment looked at the faceless figures squatted about her, then her gaze rested again on Mu San. "The wisdom of the past must be preserved. In continuity is growth," she murmured.

"Uncover your heads," said the girl. "She is gone."

Quickly the band made ready to start. A new destination was selected by Trigger. Because it was possible they might be attacked, the girl would not separate them into groups as she usually did. Trigger should lead and Shao Con and Mu San should be the last in the line except for herself.

The hill on which they had spent the day was steep and the valley in which the village stood was narrow, a mere slit between the hills. The plan which had been hastily worked out was to double back on their course, again cross the valley, but at its narrowest point, a goodly distance from the village. Stealthily they worked their way down the steep slope and onto the valley floor. The second rice crop of the season had just been harvested and the fields flooded—no moment wasted between crops in this over-populated land—frogs croaked in the paddies, mosquitoes rose in clouds, settled upon their necks, their hands. The dyke paths were narrow; turns were frequent. All this was usual and therefore comforting. Then suddenly they heard the cry echoing in the hills surrounding the valley. "Kill,

kill!" Was it a cry against them? They moved swiftly, stealthily, treading on each others' heels.

Again came the cry, "Kill, kill!" And still they must follow the precarious narrow paths raised above the rice paddies, make the abrupt turns to right, to left, follow without flinching the intricate maze of paths. At last they were on the first low slope of the hills. Suddenly, of one accord the fleeing band stood still and looked down into the valley they had crossed. Plainly they could see the village for it was lighted by torches held high by a crowd who surrounded a cart red in the glow of the torches. "Kill the woman, kill the traitor!" came the cries.

A low moan escaped the girl. It must be the woman who had come to warn them. David shivered. Mu San seemed unable to move forward.

David, treading on his heels, all at once felt a pull on his sleeve. "We are followed," the girl whispered. "Pass the word forward. Faster, faster. They're closer."

A message came back from Trigger at the head of the line. "We're near a ridge. Run for it." They tried to run, hurrying, stumbling through the undergrowth. Now, thought Mu San, now's my chance. He whirled, trying to jerk the rope from David's hands.

A rifle cracked. He fell. So suddenly did he fall that David fell against him. "Fool," whispered David, "get up."

"I'm hit."

"I've got hold of one of his shoulders. Get hold of the other," the girl commanded. The three struggled toward the ridge. One idea and one only was in David's mind—the man should not be allowed to escape and join the enemy.

One thought was in the girl's mind, but dimly understood, she must save Mu San.

When they were at last behind the ridge, they found a few of the band were already there. "Do not fire, my children, wait till they creep nearer. Bullets are precious," commanded the girl. They could hear men moving in the brush.

"Don't fire, for God's sake, don't fire," David whispered to the man next him. "Wait until they're nearer. Keep your heads down. . . ."

"Fire," cried someone. Groans, a long silence. Then bullets whistled over their heads.

The girl called out. "You are attacking the invincible maid. Go home, peasants, or she will place a curse upon you."

Uncertainty . . . doubt. The men in the scrub wavered. Then they went crashing down the hillside, for the moment more frightened of the supernatural power of the maiden than of their Communist masters who had forced them to attack her.

As the day broke, the little band looked around in dismay. They counted their losses. Six men were missing and one of them was Trigger. Just then the two Tigers crawled in among them. They brought with them rifles, cartridge belts and clothes belonging to the enemy. "Some of our own men lie among them, but we thought you would not wish us to strip them." They spoke piously.

"None were alive?" asked the girl.

"None," they answered. But in a short time two more

of their number, both wounded, came into view, crawling along as best they could.

David and the girl did what they could for the wounded. A bullet had torn the flesh on Mu San's leg, but no bones were broken. The bandages for him and for the others who were wounded had to be made from the sweat-soaked clothes the Tigers had brought. And now the girl sent the oldest peasant to bring back the clothes from their own dead, saying, "we need them."

As soon as it was dark they started the night's march, each carrying a bundle made of clothes and lumps of cold rice taken from the dead enemy. Often stopping for rest, they made their painful way toward their destination—a small monastery, two valleys away, where one of the Tigers claimed that, during the Japanese invasion, he had been taken in and cared for by the monks.

Mu San was supported by David, who himself had a surface wound in his arm which sent surges of pain up into his shoulder. But his thoughts troubled him more than his wound: without their valuable guide, Trigger, the girl must rely more upon One Eye and Two Eyes, who were the only ones left who knew this part of the country well enough to lead them. More closely than ever before must David watch that the Tigers did not separate Mu San and himself from the others.

Humbled, uncertain, the girl wavered that day in her command. She had lost face before these men. Against their judgment she had followed the advice of the woman and disaster had come upon them.

Chapter 27

BECAUSE OF THE NEED TO stop often to let the wounded rest, it took three nights and two days to reach the monastery. Toward morning of the third night's march they paused before making the last steep ascent. The valley in which they stood was still dark, but above them the mountain was lighted from behind by the rising sun. Against the glow a sheer wall of masonry stood forth boldly on the mountain's top. They began the ascent. Half-overgrown paths converged in one single path, which led to a gate in the wall. They could see it was open. Breathless, exhausted, even those who were hampered by their wounds managed to struggle up the last steep grade.

One by one, they entered the gate. Standing in an open court, they shivered in the cold mountain air. Solitude and quietness reigned here except for the winds sighing through an ancient pine. "Here we can rest. We'll have it all to ourselves. Now you know I spoke truly," said One Eye, breaking the silence.

"You are pilgrims?"

Startled, they turned and faced a monk in a faded saffron robe, who seemed to have sprung up out of the stone flagging, so quietly had he come among them.

"We seek refuge. We are guerrillas only of necessity. No longer are we welcome in the land of our forefathers."

It was an appeal simply made by the girl, for she had looked into the face of the monk and seen that he was no ignorant, degraded follower of Buddha who had helped to corrupt the faith. He had the lofty look of one who had spent his life in meditation and there was compassion in his eyes.

"I am the abbot of this monastery, and none in trouble has ever been turned away in the hundreds of years since the first of our order came here from India and built this sanctuary." As he spoke the abbot looked from the girl to the ragged group she led. "I have little to offer you, for I, too, am unwelcome in this land. I cannot accept the vows of hate which men and priests alike must now take, for such I regard the edicts which go out. There are but three of us here—only three who have remained true to their vows of chastity and mercy. We have no food except what we grow ourselves. That we will share with you. Come."

He led them across the court into a room bare of all except a long table flanked by rude benches. "Sit," he said
and left as quietly as he had come. Wearily they sank down
on the benches, their heads resting on their arms stretched
out across the table. They fell asleep, to waken to the
fragrant smell of tea. Hot tea!

Three monks moved among them, pouring hot water
onto the tea leaves in the cups placed before the exhausted
guerrillas. Again and again the monks returned with steaming kettles of water, filled the emptied cups. After a little
they came bringing bowls of rice-gruel. With sucking
sounds of satisfaction the men drew in the first hot food
they had tasted in weeks.

The abbot stood apart watching this young girl who
was evidently the leader of the band. That she was gently
born and reared was obvious both from her bearing and
speech—she had spoken to him in perfect Mandarin, the
language of the educated. He saw, too, that she was about
to break from fatigue and strain. Finally he addressed her.

"If your men will rest here for a little, I would like to
plan with you for their comfort."

The room into which he ushered her crowned the
mountaintop. It held a square table and two chairs placed
beneath the window. The paper panes of the latticed windows had been rolled up to disclose sky and mountain
peaks.

The abbot motioned the girl to be seated. She closed her
eyes, resting her head against the wall. At last she sighed
and opened her eyes and looked long at the majestic
mountains beyond the window.

"You are gently born," said the abbot. "May I know your name?" For the first time since she had left her home she spoke it. "It is Feng Mei Ing." Then she told the abbot how her father had sent her to the old tenant farmer, the original leader of the band. "My father—all my family— are dead, even the ancestral tablets have been destroyed," she ended.

"You have a foreigner among your men."

"Yes," she answered.

Then she told him of the obligation passed on to her by Old Five to return the foreigner safely to his Chinese friend in Hong Kong.

"You have a prisoner among you?"

"Yes," she said again, but she did not explain what his crime was.

"You are troubled," said the abbot. "But what is it that troubles you?"

Then she told him how against the judgment of most of the band she had followed the advice of the strange woman and thus led them into a trap.

"I think they believe that she informed the authorities. It is my first mistake. They may not trust or obey me in the future."

"The wheel of life—all must tread it," the abbot said at last.

After a little he spoke again. "I offer you all we have, but it is little." He glanced about the empty room. "Those of our order when they left took the sacred books with them. The books and the monks are now in Peking. The monks are housed in comfort, allowed to be monks only if they teach the doctrines of communism. I know not what is to happen to us who would not conform. To stay here is a risk, but if you wish to stay you may house your men in the vacant cells."

"I understand that there is a risk. But I have wounded men. They are not able now to travel. By tonight they may be."

"If that is your decision, come with me," he said and led her across a court and to a row of cells little larger, she thought, than the tiny cubicles in which scholars used to sit to take the examinations. "I will send quilts for your use," he said and left.

In the narrow cells the guerrillas threw themselves down on the bare bedboards, drew the quilts over their heads and slept. Late in the afternoon, when they woke, tea and a small portion of rice and vegetables again was given them. Then the girl, strengthened by rest and the talk with the abbot, explained that to spend the night at the monastery was dangerous. Arrests of monks and priests were made at night in order that the people should not know, so the abbot had said. She gave them their choice—they could stay here with a roof over their heads and food, but at the risk of being captured, or they could try to reach a safer place, which meant giving up the comfort here which they might never again have.

"I shall abide by your decision, for I see that some of you doubt my judgment in taking the teacher's advice."

They tried to convince her that it was because of the prisoner they would advise spending the night here—during the day he had been delirious. That he now slept after the second draft of herbs brewed by the abbot had not convinced them that he could travel. In reality they could not bring themselves to leave the shelter they had found here.

At dusk the girl sent one to watch the path which led up the mountain, one to watch a smaller gate at the side, and one to guard the cubicle where Mu San slept. Despite his delirium and weakness, no chance was to be taken on his possible escape.

David, restless because of his aching arm, slept fitfully, woke, dozed, dreamed that he was still in flight, pursued, about to be captured. Wide awake now, he listened tensely to the crackling of twigs beyond the monastery wall. Did it mean that men were creeping forward past the guards? He grasped his revolver, but presently he recognized that what he heard were the ordinary sounds of the night—the shrill cadences of insects, wind rustling a paper window-pane, a branch brushing the roof over his head. He would be still and let fear slip away—fear the environment in which daily he now lived—but he fingered his revolver. Only so did he feel safe.

When Mu San awoke from his long sleep, he thought he was back at the university. The stiff boundaries of self were giving way to oneness—he, lost in the communal self, he, a separate man about to be absorbed into the communal Godhead, a glorious Godhead, a thing of light, his indi-vidual self consumed in the brilliance of the Godhead. And then, thrust between him and the brilliance, were the flam-ing torches of the men in the valley, the death cart in their midst. He was certain who the person was who was to be

327

executed—the woman who had come to them on the hillside, who had let her eyes rest upon him when she spoke of the proud heritage of his country's history. Nonviolence was the heritage his grandfather had left him. This woman had given her life, he was convinced, to preserve that heritage. The cruel Communists had killed her. No! No! The acts of cruelty which the Godhead performed, the acts of cruelty he had been made to perform were used as abrasives to scour the vessel of the spirit, make it fit to be possessed by the collective self, the communal self.

Then the mask of light fell away from the Godhead, and Mu San saw its features were drawn in lines of evil! Gigantic evil! Man, worshipping himself and his own power, was corrupted. In horror he drew back, seeing the communal Godhead in all its dark cruelty, its beauty forever lost to him, but not the desire for it.

"Are you in pain?" It was the girl's voice. "I've come to change the bandage." In silence he watched her tip the lighted candle she held in her hand, let the wax run down on the tabletop until it made a little pool into which she set the candle. In its light he saw that her once velvety skin—the mark of the highborn woman—was blotched with mosquito bites, her lips swollen from habitual thirst, her black hair was cut short like a man's. Wearing the Lenin jacket and trousers, the cap with its visor pulled down over her eyes, the garb of the New China, she looked like a man. He'd seen thousands of women in the New China. He remembered their loud, boisterous shouts, their mannish voices; wanting no grace or beauty, and having neither. He was caught back into the knowledge of his people—man and woman distinctive, special. Man's mystic need to keep the creative forces of life separate.

The girl took from her pocket a bandage and began smearing it with a thick substance from the little pot she had placed on the ledge by the candle, and moved toward him.

"What business have you to be wearing a man's clothes?" he demanded. "You look like a man." In a kind of frenzy he poured out his disgust. "Don't come near me!"

Thinking him still delirious, she ignored his words, continued to move toward him.

"Don't touch me. If you do I'll kill you with my bare hands. You are no pure-white maiden leading men. Ha! You're a woman servicing guerrillas and peasants."

She drew back, stung by the insult. "Do not insult the men who have given me protection." Her voice was cold with contempt.

"Leave me alone," he hissed.

"I do not wish to touch you. I shall call one of the men you have insulted to care for you. You must be ready to travel. We shall not let you delay us." She left him.

He was indeed bereft! Ah, no! He would fill his empty soul with violence. Lo, his teacher, had taught him that he could lose himself in rapture by inflicting pain.

The girl was crossing the court to call one of the men to attend the prisoner when from the main temple came the abbot's voice raised almost to a shout. "I am the abbot of this monastery. I am the one you seek."

The men grasped their rifles, ran out to join the girl.

Mu San, hobbling on his swollen leg, darted this way and that among the men. Now would he taste violence! Get hold of a rifle, kill the foreigner, kill anybody else he could! Destroy! Destroy!

David, darting out of his cubicle, revolver in hand, ran toward the prisoner, grabbed him by his collar.

"Take him to the back wall," the girl commanded David. "We'll have to break through. That's our only chance."

When David, pulling the prisoner after him, reached the wall, One Eye and Two Eyes already were digging frantically with their bare hands at the old mortar, trying to loosen the half-crumbled bricks. At last they had a hole big enough for a man to crawl through. Quickly Two Eyes squirmed through the opening. Tiger One Eye whispered to David. "You first, then the prisoner."

But David pushed the girl forward, thus defeating the two Tigers in their obvious design to separate the hostages from the rest of the band and its leader.

Slowly David and the girl, pulling Mu San, worked their way down the all but perpendicular slope. Their hands, their faces bleeding, they reached the foot. Seven of the men were already there. They dared not wait for the others who might have escaped. The broken place in the wall would soon be discovered and the police would be after them. The girl turned to the two Tigers, who seemed capable of surviving every catastrophe. "Lead, you alone know this region." Running, hiding, those that were left finally, late the next day, found shelter in a shallow cave.

Chapter 28

FROM NIGHT TO NIGHT THEY were forced to postpone leaving the cave, shallow though it was. During their scramble down the mountain from the monastery, Mu San's wound had been torn open. He was running a fever. If they insisted on making him walk any distance in his present condition, he might not live to reach Hong Kong. But at the first signs that his wound was again healing all agreed to risk at least one night's travel.

They had stolen something from every farmer in the narrow valley. If the police did not hunt them out, the peasants, who knew each indentation, each rock, each hid-

331

ing place in the hills, would find them. Year after year, when the scrub grew large enough to serve as firewood, the farmers scoured the mountainsides. Why they had not done so before was probably due to the pressure upon them: morning drill, work in the fields, noon meetings, work in the fields, evening meetings—a deadly round that left them so tired they accepted fate in whatever form it took. Still there were limits even to the all but superhuman endurance of the patient Chinese. When their patience was exhausted the shao ren, the little people, attacked their adversaries savagely.

But at the end of one night's march, Mu San's leg was swollen and dark colored and he was again feverish. They must wait until he was better. This time they were quartered in a deep man-made cave which had undoubtedly been constructed by outlaws sometime passing that way. The band had little to eat and they dared not rob the nearby fields. Finally the girl, taking Tiger Two Eyes and one of the peasant guerrillas with her, went into another valley to forage. Far afield they came upon the half-ruined walls of a large farmhouse. Undoubtedly it had once belonged to a man richer than his neighbors. Probably he had been denounced by some of them during the drive against landlords. But why had the place not been completely leveled and the land put under cultivation as was usually done in such cases? The outbuildings were only half ruined, the outside compound walls were but partly demolished, bundles of brush for use under the cooking pots stood untouched in what had once been the back courtyard. "The man's ghost must have returned to protect his property," whispered Tiger Two Eyes, shivering. "Let us go quickly from here."

"Nonsense," said the girl. "We'll each take a bundle of brush. We can use them better to disguise our hiding place." As she stooped to lift a pile, her hand touched the ground underneath, and it was soft! Treasure, jewels, perhaps hastily hidden. But what good would such things do them?

"Come, let's get away from here," begged the peasant guerrilla.

"Not yet," the girl answered. By coaxing and commanding she succeeded in getting the two men to help her. Using blunt sticks they soon scattered the loose dirt. She knelt. She felt the rough surface of a burlap bag! Inside, she could feel hard separate grains. Undoubtedly rice! "There's rice here," she whispered. With their sticks they broke the bag. "Take off your jackets," she ordered. "Fill them with rice." Once Two Eyes had rice tied into his coat, he refused to stay any longer.

Knowing they were taking a risk, but unable to endure their hunger longer, they built a fire deep in the cave and, filling the one small kettle they still had with them, they cooked the rice. Time after time, they filled the kettle until they all had been fed a little.

All day they argued whether they should go back for more rice. Some contended that the ghost would not hurt them; he was only after the men who had killed him. Others insisted all ghosts were dangerous to encounter. At last the craving for rice, all their lives their staple food, overcame their fears and late in the evening, leaving David to tend and guard Mu San, they started out. Somewhat fearfully they entered the haunted ruins. Working with stout sticks and their bare hands, finally they pried some of the bags loose. They were not large and thus easily carried. Three nights they went to the deserted place, and each day on their return they risked building a small fire far back in the cave and cooked rice.

During these nights when all the others were absent David kept watch over the prisoner, but now his duty was not to guard but to care for Mu San. Grimly David performed his duty, patiently feeding rice-gruel to his enemy who, in his delirium, accepted the service, not knowing who ministered to him.

Afterwards David sat at the entrance of the cave, welcoming the privacy which he had so long been denied. Slowly, painfully, he tried to understand what had been happening during the months of his imprisonment and the months he and his rescuers had been on the march. From a Shanghai newspaper left behind by a cadre or soldier and picked up by the guerrillas on one of their nights' expeditions, also from news broadcast to the villages and which sometimes when the wind was right David had heard, he pieced together the emerging pattern. Mao Tse-tung meant to accomplish in this overpopulated land the industrial revolution more rapidly than it had ever been accomplished in any other country, even Russia. These Chinese Communists were indifferent to the suffering of the masses whom they professed to be helping. Clever men, they had tricked even the peasants into fighting for the Communist revolution. Now these same peasants were in turn to be sacrificed to the revolution which they had fought for. They had used the weapons of hatred their masters had put in their hands to destroy good landlords as well as bad in order that they might inherit the land. Bit by bit the land which they had wrested from the landlords was to be collectivized, no personal ownership allowed. Dyke paths, which were the dividing lines between one man's land and another's, would be destroyed so that machines could harvest the rice quickly and efficiently.

Memory, which had slumbered in David during the exigencies of the march, was again awakened and he remembered words written by his father not long before his death. "Emily saw more clearly than I that the industrial knowledge of the West would not come to China as I first believed it would. I now know it will be a gigantic, violent creature bursting forth from China's old womb, tearing and destroying it in the moment of birth."

Pondering on his father's words, David saw that all who belonged to China—men, women and children—would be distorted by the violence of revolution. Why, that was what had happened to Mu San. Again, as once on the junk, David felt compassion for the young Chinese. Compassion for Mu San who had destroyed the underground and denied David his hard-won opportunity to make atonement to Paul Damon! Never!

Memory of those hours he had stood before Mu San in that room in Shanghai came back. David's victory in not betraying his country, as night after night Mu San tried to make him do so, seemed no victory now. How could he be sure that in time he would not have broken under the strain of torture? Only that unproved loyalty to set against the many accusations Mu San had brought to prove that David was a traitorous man. Mu San had used every weapon he had to bring irreparable injury to David's faith in himself—a wound too deep for healing. The guilt lying deep in every man—residue of the disobediences of childhood, acts hidden away from his mother, his father, indistinct, dark, terrible, strange tormenting anxieties, augmented the mistakes and subterfuges of later years, those years of compromise leading up to his betrayal of Paul Damon.

Mu San had done this terrible thing to him. Pistol in hand, David crawled toward the entrance to the cave where Mu San lay undefended, at last at David's mercy. Hate and revenge would now have their chance. Suddenly he drew back. What was he about to do? Betray this band of desperate, fleeing men and their valiant leader? Sunder the ties which bound them together? What kind of man was he? Words not of his own making, cried within him, "There is a man inside me who is angry with me."

Chapter 29

NOT DARING TO WAIT LONGER, the next night the band moved back into the range of hills where the mountains were higher, the valleys narrower, the villages smaller and more scattered. Their progress was now hampered by their bundles of rice and the necessity of carrying Mu San on a crude litter. When at last the Tigers brought them to a deeper cave, the girl ordered that they wait here until the sick man was stronger. The wound was at last healing and he could soon travel without risk to his health. They were comparatively safe here, for now that they had rice they did not need to steal so much from the farmers.

During the day, when the others lay asleep in the cave, the girl often worked her way down the slope where she could watch the peasants threshing the rice by simply knocking the heads against rude boxes set in the fields. Toward evening water buffaloes, after a day's work, soaked themselves in the ponds, their noses and curved horns lying upon the dark surface of the water—peaceful farm scenes which helped her to feel how deep the roots of her family were sunk into China's countryside. By some delicate inner perception she brought harmony to herself through the sense of union with the fertility of the earth.

One night she took the midnight watch outside the cave. Sitting huddled in a quilt to keep off the mosquitoes, she felt deeply disturbed. Futile indeed seemed the high purpose she had held when she took over the leadership of the band. In the beginning she had carried out the mission as she felt her father would have done. He, a member of the underground, had rescued those who were in danger; she had rescued a few, but now that the myth that she was invulnerable had been destroyed and she was known to the people merely as leader of a band who plundered their fields, she felt little better than the destructive Tigers, who she knew were trying to destroy the loyalty to her so necessary to the survival of them all.

And it troubled her that she had ministered exclusively to the prisoner, leaving the American and the other members of the band who had been wounded to be nursed by the men. Useless to hide any longer behind the excuse that Mu San needed her special care because he was critically ill while the others were not. She loved this prisoner

338

who had brought so much evil to her family and to his own. Now, even as when she bathed his face and hands, she felt the delicate bone structure of his face, his long, slender fingers, so different from the heavy-structured faces and blunt fingers of the peasants in the band. He seemed to be the embodiment of the grace and beauty of her people and yet he was the betrayer. And she loved him. It was evil of her to love this man who was evil. Yet huddled there on the hillside she continued to yield to the enchantment of his touch, remembering how his hand had lain so helpless in hers as she tended him.

Inside the cave Mu San woke, his mind at last clear, conscious of renewed bodily vigor. He was young and his body had thrown off the wound's infection. There had been moments of consciousness during his delirium when he realized that he had been gently ministered to by the girl. Did she love him? If so, he could use her love to destroy her leadership over the band. Once she was no longer inviolate, the men would get to wrangling among themselves over her. In the chaos which would ensue, he would escape with her, make her plunder for him. Both would become outlaws. He would drag her down with him into degradation.

Tonight he would seek her out where she slept separate from the others and take her before the strict discipline she exerted over herself when awake had time to dominate her love for him. But first he would enjoy his freedom— he had not been bound during his sickness—walk a little in the fresh air outside the cave with its sick and unwashed and enjoy the havoc soon to be wrought by him.

The girl, instantly alert to any movement, demanded in a whisper, "Who leaves the cave?"

Then Mu San laughed recklessly, a laugh deep within him, the muscles of his stomach contracting and expanding, but no sound came. He saw an even more interesting way to destroy her. Make her destroy herself by voluntarily yielding to him. "Sh, it is only the poor prisoner come to watch with you and repay the many times you have ministered to him."

"You are abusing my confidence in you." The girl spoke sternly. "You know that it is only because I wished to make you more comfortable during your sickness that you have not been shackled."

"You are here to guard me. Is that not enough?" He sat down close to her. "Have pity on me, I am lonely as only a prisoner can be. I am so lonely! You would not deny me a woman's compassion." Again that silent inner laughter.

"Lonely," she mocked. "You, who long ago sank your identity in that of the State. Alone? Why, you can never be alone."

"You're as bad as those you condemn. You're not human. If you were, you would offer me the love that comes from compassion."

"You don't know what you are saying. You've betrayed all those who love you and now you want to talk to me of love . . . without its responsibilities," she added, bitterness in her voice.

"Let us live while we can. We are young. All these

340

others are old. They don't mean anything to us. We are already outlaws." He reached out his hand and grasped the quilt she clasped so tightly.

Suddenly she flung out her hand and pinned his to his side. Her strength was greater than his this evening.

Angrily he denounced her. "You're just like a man. I despise masculine women."

Stung by his words she retorted, "You Communists have forced women to be like men, defying the knowledge of our people. Women have their special place in the universe. It's you who have taken it from them. Did you ever look beneath the visors of the caps Communist women wear pulled down over their eyes? Did you ever look into their eyes? Try it sometime. You won't find in them any gentleness, nor any compassion for a man's loneliness. You'll see only cruelty in their eyes. I'd rather be captured by one of the Communist men. I'd fare better than at the hands of such distorted women."

"I did not make the revolution," Mu San retorted.

"Get back into the cave," she commanded.

The next night as she sat outside he crept stealthily toward her, driven now by the urgent demand of his body to possess her. He was almost upon her when she whispered, "I shall call to the men if you come closer."

Angered, more determined than ever, he crept back into the cave.

On the third night he whispered to her from a distance. "I place myself at your mercy. I am indeed alone. I'm no longer acceptable to the Party. I'm no longer acceptable

341

to my father. I—I cannot bear it," he cried out. "Shelter me. Bring me back to the ways of my people."

"I am not the one to judge you. That is for your honorable father. To him I must deliver you."

A low groan escaped Mu San.

"I—I—Mu San." The girl stammered and when he fumbled at the quilt, wrapped so closely around her, she made no move to fling his hand away. Instead she let him creep within and lie close to her and she drew the quilt around them both. There was no resistance in her, moved by passion as he was.

But when he left her, she wept. She had let him have his way with her and he did not love her. Back at the temple, he had told her what he really thought of her when he would not allow her even to touch him. He had taken her in contempt and derision while she, consumed with desire to feel him against her—his slender body so like her own—had let him come within her defenses. She could have held him back. After the first time he had joined her outside the cave, she had only to issue orders that he be bound at night but she had not done it. She had betrayed the trust Old Five had put in her.

To Mu San's surprise and anger in the morning, she went before her men and said, "I have chosen my mate from among you and my choice is the prisoner. You can trust me. I shall see that he is more closely guarded than ever. From now on he shall be shackled whether sick or well."

"The prisoner! You defiled yourself by choosing the prisoner!" cried the magistrate she had rescued.

"They can sleep under one quilt now. We can use the extra one," said one of the peasants who had not had a blanket to himself.

"Mei yu fat su," said Tiger One Eye, secretly pleased. The girl was no longer the Maiden. They need not respect her any longer.

"Mei yu fat su, it can't be helped," the others echoed and laughed. They were rough, earthy men who, secretly, admired the prisoner's prowess.

Only David was angry. Mu San had brought a new evil upon them all. It would not be that the men would rebel against the girl's leadership which was what he believed Mu San meant to accomplish—her words, spoken so valiantly, had salvaged something of her power over the men—David sensed that from now on she would not be as certain of herself as she had been before. Her singleness of purpose had been destroyed and gradually she would relinquish her authority. If only he had killed Mu San that night when he lay sick and defenseless. Mu San deserved to die. He had brought only evil and dissension. He was like a goat prancing ahead of David, pulling hard at the rope, sometimes forcing David to run. He should die, yet if he died the reason for this journey south would die with him. So he must live—this beast who should be driven into the wilderness to make atonement—scape— escape, David corrected his thoughts, escape should not be granted him.

Mu San felt a reckless pride in what he had done. He revelled in his knowledge that the girl was his. He would soften her until she was no longer able to rule. He had only to wait. And he delighted in making it difficult for David to keep up with him.

Chapter 30

THE BAND WAS RESTED AND better nourished now and Mu San was strong enough to endure the night marches. They must hurry on, for it would soon be autumn and then winter—winter with its cold rains for which they were unprepared. And there would be no place to hide once the peasants began to come to the hills for firewood. Day by day the band seemed to be more under control of the two Tigers. The territory they were covering was thoroughly known only to these two. It was in this region they had operated before joining the farmer guerrillas. The Tigers led the band to cleverly disguised hiding places and also to ponds where water

345

chestnuts could be pulled up from the slimy bottoms and fish corrals where fish could be stolen from the nets set out at night. The men now plundered at will. David believed the Tigers had actually killed the magistrate who tried to keep them from unnecessary plundering. Was it the plan of these two to reduce their numbers one by one until none were left except themselves and their hostages?

Then when the Tigers seemed to have taken the leadership from the girl, her indecision, which had been more and more evident as the days went by, was suddenly gone. The night's march had been overly long. Daylight overtook them. Hurrying to reach their hiding place, without stopping to reconnoiter they rounded a projection of rocks and Tiger One Eye, who was leading, faced an old man.

As One Eye raised his rifle to shoot, with a quick decisive movement the girl stepped in front of him saying to the old man, "I am commander of this band. I wish to know who you are. I see there are children and women with you. If villagers, return to your houses and your farms and do not speak of us to your rulers, from whom we are fleeing."

"Ah," spoke the old man. "You, like us, eat bitterness. We have escaped from a valley a few days' journey away. We fled in haste."

"Let us then confer together," said the girl. "It is possible we can serve each other. Tell us first of conditions. It has been long since we have talked with anyone."

The old man had a mole on his cheek from which a few long black hairs reached down to his chest; he was of the old school which believed such a mole brought luck. From his clothes it was evident that he was not used to poverty; although his garments showed wear, they were good garments. He motioned the men and women of his party to come forward and squat around him.

The girl motioned her men to squat on the ground near her. "Can you tell us why you fled?" she asked.

"Our sons were sent to fight in Korea. This we had been led to believe was necessary in order to guard against the outside barbarians." (David pulled his cap lower.) "Now for another war far to the south our sons are caught when working in the fields and made to serve the State. Heavier taxes are being exacted of us and there are rumors that our land no longer is to be ours. In districts in the North already the boundaries of the fields have been destroyed. The great landlord, this Mao Tse-tung, although he himself was once a peasant, would gather all of the land of the Black Haired People unto himself! A peasant woman who was sent north because her land yielded more than other fields saw it all. A mighty machine was sent over the wheat fields and into its great mouth it took the harvest. Not even one grain was left behind for the poor. And when the monster had gone the fields were one field and no man knew his own land. There were no boundaries." The man spat and cursed.

"Already strange young men and women have come among us, urging that we join together our time and our animals. Bah!" The man spat again. "This we were too smart to do. First the tools, the animals, and then the land would be taken. This we would not do. Then a whisper began that we were counterrevolutionaries. I and my family

347

were the leaders. A meeting was to be called. The village would be made to give judgment against us. I and my wife and my family were to be sent to hard labor, one to one camp, one to another. And the family would be destroyed. Never again should I see my sons or my son's sons. One son has already been killed in the war in the South. I have not told you the worst. The family, like the land, is to be done away with, that a family called the State may be created. Like the land, no boundaries. The wells are full of daughters, wives, and concubines. They have joined the ancestors that the family may be preserved." He stopped talking, his head sank on his breast.

"And so you fled?"

"And so we fled. There are great mountains to the west where we can hide for years undiscovered—so we have been told. We're farmers. We know how to terrace little pockets in the hillsides. We have seed rice with us." He rose, motioned to those around him to rise. "We go north and west," said the old man in final salutation.

How could they survive, with women not used to mountain trails, children who would cry and give them away? thought the girl and renewed resolution came to her. Only on last night's march had she accepted the fact that she was pregnant. They must hurry on, get out of the country before her child was born. She would lead again and with force and decision.

From now on she governed these men as the mothers of China had governed their households: Even when they were sick or tired, she made them exert their wills over their bodies, but in some mysterious way she also succored

348

them, providing the strength they needed. These men, who had been reared to the authority of the matron in their households, began to regard her with real deference. It was as if somehow she had become the head of the clan to which they all belonged and they began to call her Tai Tai, "the Head Woman." Even the Tigers realized she was the power that forced the band forward toward their goal. David, born and brought up under the tutelage of amah, understood the deference and obedience now accorded to her, but he wondered at the miracle so suddenly wrought in her.

Mu San, who had heretofore weakened himself and her by his plaintive, sentimental pleas, playing upon her love for him, began to find her love stern and demanding, but it offered him a strange, not understood, rehabilitation. Slowly his desire to destroy the band through her left him. But not his hatred for the foreigner.

Summer was over. Present in all their minds was the threat of winter with its cold rains from which they had no protection, no roof to shelter them, no warm clothes to keep out the cold and the rain. They moved more rapidly now, for their band was steadily growing smaller. Two had died, and the eldest guerrilla had disappeared during a foraging expedition.

It was nearing the time for the Eight Moon Festival. Each night the harvest moon was growing larger and fuller. The moon, the sun's cool companion, for long centuries had been regarded as a feminine deity—the two, sun and moon, a heavenly couple in charge of the world and its

affairs. Mao Tse-tung, the new father of his people, knowing the value of tradition and symbolism, used each festival to bind the people more closely to the State—emotions
engendered through memory perverted to serve the State.

With the moon to guide them, Tigers One and Two led
the guerrillas—a constantly shrinking number—quickly up
hill and down. But when the night came that the moon was
full, the woman demanded they pause to make their
obeisance to the heavenly couple—an act which seemed
necessary to her. One Eye and Two Eyes agreed without
a murmur, not because they wished to celebrate, but because they detected that the precious foreigner was losing
strength. He needed time to rest. This moonlit night they
would rest in a fold in the hills—protection enough from
the village below. The moon riding high illumined its one
street.

When evening came a cadre arrived for the festival.
They walked among the villagers saying, "Little brothers
and sisters, be happy, rejoice in the new and glorious State.
Let us dance and sing. See, we are dressed in the new and
beautiful cottons that now are manufactured for your
use!" One wore a Lenin jacket, stamped with the pattern
of the Strutting Peacock, and one a jacket with a scene of
new farm life—tractors standing in fields unbroken by
boundary lines. "Comrades, you have earned beauty. These
lovely things are now being created for you. Dance and
sing."

But the faces of men and women bathed in moonlight
held more than the usual lines of care. Despite the new ways

of ploughing, better seed supplied by the State, and the promise of a rich harvest, they were worried, for after the rice tax was delivered there would not be enough rice left to live on until the next harvest. A bigger tax than ever before was to be paid because the State was threatened anew, they had been told, by America, by its imperialism, by its brutality, by its intention to invade China. Therefore Indo-China must be brought into the Communist world.

After the dancing and singing, when the families gathered for the traditional feast, few children were with them. From the police station at the end of the village street came young voices, the voices of their children, singing the new songs. Their children, their boys and girls, too young yet to be sent to war, had been gathered together by the cadre. The final insult, the final mockery! They, the peasants who had brought about the revolution, who had killed the landlords by order of Father Mao, were now being told out of one corner of his mouth, to rejoice with the moon—and that meant rejoice with their children—while out of the other corner of his mouth, through the cadre, Father Mao was saying to their children, "The duty to fathers and mothers is to be replaced by duty to the great Father Mao," creator of a new China, the new State. The voices of their children rang out,

"Mao Tse-tung like the sun brings joy to us all,
Makes our lives so warm and happy.
Behold, oh behold, our beloved, beloved moon!
China is our motherland."

351

There was the loss of their children, and the moon cakes tasted of rancid oil, a final insult at celebration time. Suddenly they were through with a submission which sent to Russia food they should be eating, they and their children! House doors were flung open, men and women rushed out, knives and sickles in their hands, and stormed the police station. Cries and groans reached the remnant of the band on the hillside.

"Ai yah," gasped Tiger One Eye, "the moment has come when the peasants' endurance explodes! Let us go now to the town. In the commotion we will loot and bring back food."

"I will not go," said the woman, "I shall sit here."

"Leave you alone with our hostages while the rest of us forage!" Both of the Tigers spoke in outraged unison.

"You are as necessary to us as we to you," she answered. "We know not the way. We would soon be lost in the mountains."

"Lost, indeed," the two echoed as they left with the remnants of the band.

From their vantage point on the hill above the town David, Mu San and the woman watched flames leap high. "The people have risen. Now there is hope," softly the woman spoke.

"What use will it be? For centuries in chaotic times the peasants have risen only to be put down," said Mu San.

Ignoring his remark, the woman said, "I shall soon be heavy with child. When the Tigers observe it, I shall no longer be safe. One of you must always be on watch. Shao Con," she said, turning to David, "you must persuade the Tigers that Mu San must no longer be tied to you on the march. Tell them it hampers you and the extra strain wears upon you."

David did not answer. What reason was there to trust Mu San? What evidence did anyone have of his sincerity?

Mu San felt for a moment the desire of his people for a son. The family perpetuated. His delight sobered into responsibility. The mother of his child must be protected. The effrontery of the Tigers who would destroy the woman who carried his child! Barbaric men knowing nothing of human relationship. Human relationship? A sudden groping in the world where human relationships had existed for him.

At dawn One Eye staggered up the hill under a load of food and a couple of rifles. "Here, my children, is your feast. Moon cakes, a few peanuts, cooked rice—hot rice."

"Where are the others?" the woman asked.

"I know not," said Two Eyes. "There is much blood being shed. Government troops have arrived in the town. Many of the people have already been shot, some hanged. The oldest peasant among us I saw lying in a pool of blood. I mourn him greatly. We were friends."

"And where is Two Eyes? Did you see him?"

"We can't wait for him," said One Eye, "deeply as I long to save my brother. The government is broadcasting that the revolt is the work of guerrillas. The peasants, they say, fought bravely for the motherland. The troops are to scour the hills. They say that Americans started the trouble. We must quickly get out of this region."

Then Two Eyes crawled out of the brush. But none of the others returned.

Only the five were left now. Their desperate flight lasted for days, up one hill, down another, for the government was searching for any peasants who had escaped to join guerrillas. Both David and Mu San were still hampered by the rope which had so long held them together. Each night now when David picked up the rope with Mu San tethered to the other end he felt shame, yet he could not give back to Mu San the dignity of a man. "He is too guilty, and how do we know that he can be trusted?" he asked himself.

Then one morning Mu San turned upon David. "I am the father of the child who is to be born, and I mean to protect the woman who bears him."

Then and then only did David say to the Tigers, "I am not equal to the strain upon me," and he added, "The prisoner should carry a rifle. It is silly for each of you to be burdened with two rifles and a strong man among us go unarmed. We may, at any time, be attacked."

The two Tigers consulted together. They knew the foreigner spoke truly of his lack of strength, but still they did not wish to give Mu San the advantage of freedom, a rifle and ammunition. Did he suspect them of wishing to be rid of the woman? Finally, they decided, they must not tax the foreigner's waning strength. But still they hoped to find some way of accomplishing their purpose. Five were too many to cross the valley to the delta. Five were too many for one sampan in which they planned to drift down to the coast.

When at last the peasants were quiet, subdued if not

conquered, and over the loud-speakers the announcement came that the hills had been cleared of the wicked guerrillas, the Tigers suggested that the prisoner should give up the rifle.

"Can you be sure we will not be attacked?" asked David. "The prisoner is less dangerous than outside enemies. He certainly does not wish to be handed over to men who commit such cruelties as have been committed against the peasants who had been captured." Still David spoke only for the sake of the woman, he still harbored his hatred for Mu San, although he now trusted him.

Whenever the woman joined the Tigers in foraging for food, Mu San insisted that he accompany her. The Tigers objected, saying, "We can't risk the prisoner's life in so dangerous an undertaking." But David and Mu San, now cooperating with each other for the sake of the woman, were firm. It ended by one Tiger going with the prisoner and the woman; the other accompanied David to their destination.

Relentless as the Tigers were in trying to get rid of the woman who handicapped them, they were more and more solicitous of the foreigner who also handicapped them, but he held value for them and she did not. Their consideration for David was boundless. They saw to it that he was given the best food brought in, they nursed him during his attacks of malarial fever. When he was shaken with a chill, they took off their own ragged jackets and put them over his shoulders. In the daytime when they lay among the scrub, they picked the fleas first from their own jackets and then helped him to do the same to his, so that whether he wore their jackets, or his own, he was saved the itching which seemed to take toll of his ebbing strength.

David now came to feel that for the woman's sake he *must* complete the journey. Only so could these two ruthless men get the ransom they were after. If once they felt he would be unable to reach Hong Kong, they would take off on their own, leaving the three to wander hopelessly in mountains which they did not know. Every bit of will power he could muster, David now exerted to complete each night's march. He managed it somehow, but when the day came exhaustion would take over and his will to survive was all but vanquished by the longing, growing greater each day, never to rise from the earth upon which he lay. But, somehow, when night came he found strength to rise once more.

During these days Mu San, watching over the woman, could not say whether he loved her or not. It was enough just now that she carried his child. If he did not love her, at least he felt responsible for her. And once, when David was awake and had indicated he would watch over the woman, Mu San fell asleep and dreamed that he came voluntarily into the presence of his father and the woman was with him. She was no longer dressed in the jacket, garb of another country, but in the long gown of her own people and she carried their son in her arms. "Oh, my father," he cried, "I have come back, and I come by the grace of this woman. I have chosen her to be my wife, and we bring our son with us." And then he had wakened to see this woman, the leader of the band, in a ragged Lenin jacket, her black hair rusty and untidy.

At last they were nearing the place where they would leave the mountains and cross the valley leading to the delta of the Pearl River and the coastal plain beyond. David was aware that he might use his weakness to help the woman. If the Tigers were made to realize that they never could get him to Hong Kong and their hope of a ransom was gone, they might come to believe that it was not worth risking the dangers incurred in leaving the hills and would decide to desert the three and leave them to starve. It was a desperate hope but David thought it worth trying. By it he might save the woman's life, for from now on the Tigers would use more and more ruthless methods to get rid of her. But first he must learn the route to be followed after they left the mountain ranges and came into more open country. Each day now he made capital of his ebbing strength, asking extra services of the Tigers, playing upon their credulity, hoping to raise doubt in their minds of his ability to complete the journey. He would say, "When we get to the valley which leads to the delta it won't be so hard for me, will it, with no climbing to do? I can make better time then?"

"Yes," they would assure him. "There are hills, but the land between is flat."

"And do we have to go far each night?" The number of miles they mentioned was not many.

"Ah, I see," said David. "You measure distance as the true Chinese count it. If it is flat, the distance is not so great."

"Verily you are right and you are clever," they answered.

357

"But where can we hide?" he would ask, saying, "It gives me courage to be able to think of shelter. I shall need rest."

And patiently, seeing he was fearful of the journey, they would describe the hiding places to him. "There's a pavilion for the first day, stacked high with coffins taken from the fields," they told him. "Somehow we must squeeze you all behind them. The pile is high, but the space is narrow."

"But surely five are not too many." David raised his voice so that Mu San would hear and be extra vigilant in his care of the woman.

"And there are groves, you say, thicker than those farther north?"

One or the other Tiger would describe, for the encouragement of this timorous foreigner, the palmetto groves fringed with thick-growing bamboo where they would hide.

"And during the day I can look across the flat land and see the next grove?"

"Yes."

So little by little, bit by bit, David pieced together the route they must take after they left the continuous mountain ranges and what they must do when they reached the delta.

"In the delta you can hide, Little Sick One. It's a paradise for fugitives—mango and palmetto trees hang their branches low. It's a jungle of trees and vines. Pirates for centuries have hidden there. All we have to do is steal a sampan and drift from one old canal or stream to another. You can rest all day and all night in the bottom of the sampan, Little Sick One." Here now was the first indication that

358

they were beginning to fear he would not be able to finish the journey. The diminutive often used by the Chinese to indicate contempt was creeping more and more into their talk.

Mu San, watching, did not know what to think. The dark cloud of hatred for the foreigner obscured his vision. Was this Conway going to let them down? Fail them in this moment of crisis?

As the time drew near when he must convince the Tigers that their chance of getting him to Hong Kong was too slim to risk the danger of their leaving the hills, David grew fearful of the success of his plan. He counted on the Tigers' deserting them, fleeing back into the hills, but there was a chance that, in their anger, they would attempt to shoot the three of them. It was a terrible risk that he was taking. He thought of the little jockey. Te Lin would take such a gamble.

Early one morning Tiger One Eye pointed out to the foreigner the valley they must cross. All that day David lay, feigning weakness. As night came, he began to plead for a little more time in which to gain strength for the forced marches ahead of them. "I must rest," he gasped. "Perhaps you had better go on without me."

"You would fail us now when we are so near!" One Eye kicked him in rage. David staggered to his feet, fell backwards.

Suddenly Mu San grasped what David was trying to do. "Leave him alone," he commanded. "It's not too much to let him rest until he is stronger. One night or two won't matter."

The Tigers lay down grumbling. Soon David heard them snoring. Was it real or only a pretense?

David dared not sleep. He clutched his pistol under his worn coat, hoping that his companions were equally ready. He heard stealthy movements away from them. Were the Tigers abandoning them? Through the rest of the night he watched, fearing one of the Tigers might have hidden to take them unawares when day came. In the first faint light of day, David saw they were alone. He let his pistol fall from his hand. His ruse had worked. The pair had fled, undoubtedly believing that they had left the helpless trio to die from want of guidance. David's knowledge of the Chinese had proved correct: the two outlaws would enjoy thinking of the slow death of their victims; it would give them more pleasure than they would get from shooting them outright—too quick a death.

All day the woman did what she could for David, who lay on the ground exhausted from the night's vigil. From a nearby mountain spring not entirely dried up she brought water and bathed his face and hands. She made him eat the few stale moon cakes she had saved, stolen by Tiger Two Eyes the night of the festival. Most of the food they had laboriously accumulated for the rest of their flight the outlaws had taken with them.

David, looking at her in the ragged coat, pushed outward by the child growing within her, at her black eyes, caverned by her cheekbones which jutted out from her painfully thin face, felt an overpowering desire to understand woman's meaning for a man. Before him passed the women who had been close to him in his life: his mother, amah,

Miriam. He thought of his mother's effort to protect him; of amah, who had given him of her love and mercy; of Miriam . . . he had taken from Miriam, giving little in return. Suddenly he saw that his incomplete relationship to her had brought him to his betrayal of Damon.

Not far from him were the woman and Mu San, half hidden by a rise of ground. Their low-spoken words reached him. He heard Mu San say, "I do not have to go back to my father now." And the woman's reply, "Only if you choose to present your son to him." And then it seemed to David from where he lay as if Mu San placed his hand in hers—a rare gesture for a Chinese to make.

Astonishing, David thought, at this time with an all but impossible journey still ahead of them, these two, so young, were confident of escape, of life itself, of a son to make their union complete and project them on into immortality. Had they forgotten that they must go down into the valley where no one would dare, even if he wished, to give them food? The officials could check on as much as a cup of rice diverted from the uses for which it was designed. Eventually they must somehow secure something that would float, and on it drift on the shallow streams and old canals running through the swampy land of the delta, and they must enter the wide Pearl River and somewhere find a canal leading across the coastal plain. Finally they would have to throw themselves on the mercy of the authorities in Macao, to be given asylum or be turned back.

Again David heard the voices of the two mingling. Words drifted to him—"a new life, a better life." And for the first time he noticed how emaciated Mu San was.

361

The woman had washed his jacket and laid it in the sun to dry. Seeing the marks on Mu San's skin where the rope had rubbed, David looked away.

Suddenly he was swept with compassion for this young Chinese, still holding to the dream of another opportunity. This time there was a cleansing in David's compassion. The guilt which so long had bound him to Mu San with hate was gone, and also the angry man within himself was gone; his compassion covered them both.

A verse his mother often had made him repeat came to him, "In the secret place of the Most High." And he rose and went a little apart from these two who were whispering together of life, and he came to a rock, and he knelt behind it, and looked down on the valley beginning to grow dark—the still Chinese countryside, so fruitful, producing here in the South its four crops a year. Banana groves dotted the plain. The rice paddies were just now coming to fruition. The intricate network of dykes set each man's field apart. He saw the thin lines of smoke rising over the villages. It's time for the evening meal, he thought.

Looking at the rich Chinese earth used for centuries and kept fertile he remembered the teaching of his childhood. The whole earth fecund with life, all in the universe either male or female. Creation was a process going on in him, in the earth beneath his feet, in each insignificant thing of the universe. And then he thought of the three he had left behind on the hillside. Yes, he thought of them as three now. There was something he must do for them because he, like them, had his part in the universe.

In what did it lie? Light, and darkness, each carrying within itself the essence of the other, created the harmony of life. Earth, the tilled field which takes up the seed of heaven. Also death and life together creating. Death—was it his portion to stand opposite to life? He laid his arms across the rock, and bowed his head upon them. Darkness was all around him. He saw that there would come a time— just when, he did not know—after they went down into the less protected country, a time when one must be given to save the others. . . . Mu San and the woman, if possible, must live and the child with them. He rose and joined the others, saying, "It is time."

In safety they reached the first day's hiding place—the pavilion the Tigers had described. Indeed, the quarters were close behind the high-piled coffins. None of them dared to sleep; none of them could sleep on the cold stone floor. But when night came and it was quiet, they prepared to move on to the next stopping place—a grove. "Not long now," he told himself. Now he must try to make his peace with Mu San. "I do not know whether you will accept it," he whispered, speaking with some difficulty, "but before we start, I could wish that there be friendship between us."

After a long pause Mu San spoke stiffly, "You are my father's friend and as such I accept the friendship." The woman spoke gently, saying, "Shao Con, you are one of us." I am asking too much, thought David. He is still maimed from his experience—as I am. The woman will lead him out to—yes, I believe, to wholeness.

Three days and nights: all had gone as David had

planned, and then on the fourth night he lost his way. When day came he saw that the first patch of jungle was too far away to be reached. "We'll have to hide in the grain," he said. "I'm sorry."

"It's not ready for harvesting. From a distance we cannot be detected. The peasants won't come to the fields today," the woman assured him. "Tonight we can reach the delta. See, it's to the left."

Carefully they crawled into a field and lay some distance apart, each straightening the grain behind and around him so as to leave as small an indentation as possible. They chewed the half-ripe rice heads, drank sparingly of the water they had brought with them. The fields remained silent.

It was late in the afternoon when they heard voices. Two men, father and son, from their conversation, had come to judge when the rice would be ready for cutting. "Ai yah!" they suddenly exclaimed as they looked down and saw Mu San's still figure amidst the grain. "Ai yah!" they shouted. "You've ruined us! We can't make our quota! Get out of our field!"

Mu San raised his rifle. "Before I shoot, leave this spot. Go back to your village and say nothing about me. Sing your song of rejoicing, sing of the richness of the coming harvest as you go. I shall not be here if you come back. If you say you saw a man in your field, the police will say you were lying to cover up shortage." The two turned and went back over the path by which they had come. Waveringly their song rose.

David, crawling close to Mu San, said, "I see no one else

on the dyke paths. You and the woman must start now. Walk as fast as you can. As I cannot walk fast enough I will hide in the next field until it's dark."

"We'll not go without you, Shao Con," whispered the woman.

"It's the only way I can escape. I have to have time," David answered. "They'll see you in the distance but they won't be able to catch up with you and they won't look for me."

"It's a desperate plan, but it may work," Mu San answered, sensing what it was David was doing for him and the woman. "Come," he said, "mother of my child."

The sun was near setting. No one could be seen. Smoke rose over the village. The evening meal was being prepared. Evidently the two men had kept silent. Then suddenly there was the animallike sound a mob makes. Mu San and the woman knew that sound and began to run. David heard it and knew what he had to do. Now, now expiation! Return for friendship! He crawled to the edge of the field and waited. The roar of the mob grew louder. He climbed up the embankment and stood on the path, clearly revealed to them.

"There he is," the crowd bellowed.

David slid down the embankment on the other side of the path, struck into a dyke path which ran in an opposite direction to the one which would have taken him toward the jungle.

The crowd jumped down into the field, fanned out, raced along the intricate dykes seeking to head him off.

Mustering all his strength, David made one final effort to get beyond them. He had them all behind him now and he led them back toward the village—running, but not really running, walking in his own dignity! He turned to face them, let them draw near enough so that they could see him clearly. "I am the one you seek," he called out in a loud voice.

"An outside man! Foreign devil!" shrieked the mob. "Kill him!"

Their cries of hatred reached the two fugitives. They stopped in their flight and looked back. A pistol shot rang out. They saw David standing alone. Saw him half turn, topple, fall.

A cry broke from the woman.

"Come on," cried Mu San, "don't waste his sacrifice." He took her hand and pulled her forward, running, panting. The swamp was nearer now. The cries of the mob grew fainter.

The man and woman dashed in among the underbrush. They burrowed deep in the tangled underbrush. The night mist crept around them. They lay, listening for the mob which did not come, holding each other close. "For us Shao Con gave his life," whispered the woman.

Slowly, painfully Mu San sought to surrender his last vestige of hatred for the man of the West. Suddenly he remembered an angry Chinese youth standing on a hilltop in Hong Kong, telling this man who had just died for them that he stood for Christian man and that he had lost his soul. So he died to get it back, thought Mu San, a little scornfully. Then he was ashamed.

366

"Mother of my child," he whispered, "we can wait no longer. Shao Con told us we must hurry." A little awkwardly he spoke David's Chinese name, which never before had he allowed to pass his lips.